CANTATE DOMINO

CANTATE DOMINO

FULL MUSIC EDITION
CHORAUSGABE · EDITION CHORALE

AN ECUMENICAL HYMN BOOK
EIN ÖKUMENISCHES GESANGBUCH
PSAUTIER ŒCUMÉNIQUE

New edition · Neue Ausgabe · Nouvelle édition

Published on behalf of the
World Council of Churches

Veröffentlicht im Auftrag des
Ökumenischen Rates der Kirchen

Publiée sous le patronage de
Conseil œcuménique des églises

OXFORD UNIVERSITY PRESS

*Printed in Great Britain
at the University Press, Oxford
by Eric Buckley
Printer to the University*

Table of Contents · Inhaltsverzeichnis
Table des Matières

Foreword

CHRISTIANITY was born in song. The songs of Mary, Elizabeth, the angels and Simeon heralded the birth of Christ. On that fateful evening when Jesus had his last supper with the disciples they sang a hymn before going out to face the final encounter with betrayal and death. After Pentecost the new Christian community shared their life together 'with glad and generous hearts, praising God'. Throughout its history the vigour of the Church's life and of its renewal has been marked by Christians 'addressing one another in psalms and hymns and spiritual songs, singing and making music to the Lord' (Ephesians 5:19).

'Singing and making music to the Lord' is an act of thanksgiving, acknowledging the mighty acts of grace of the God and Father of our Lord Jesus Christ. It is something we can delight in doing together, a demonstration of our common life in one Body, reconciled and held together by Christ the Head through the Holy Spirit. No wonder the modern ecumenical movement should find its most popular expression in Christians singing each other's hymns.

Already in 1924, the World Student Christian Federation, that pace-setter of the ecumenical movement, published a first edition of *Cantate Domino*, which remained for fifty years its most widely used publication. Noble efforts were made in successive editions, especially that of 1951, to make the book more adequately representative of the world Christian community. Yet, despite the inclusion of some Asian hymns, it was found impossible properly to adapt such music to an 'international' style, and this was considered 'an unsolved problem of ecumenical hymnody'.

As Chairman of the W. S. C. F. in the 1960s, when the pressure was felt for a new edition, I was involved in the discussions and the eventual decision, in 1968, that the task of revision was beyond the time, competence and resources of a mainly student organisation. Since *Cantate Domino* had also become in practice the hymn book of the World Council of Churches, it was appropriate to ask the Uppsala Assembly of the Council to take on the responsibility, which it bravely did, entrusting the project to its Faith and Order Commission. I am therefore delighted to greet this new edition and commend it for use around the world.

'*Cantate Domino canticum novum*—Sing to the Lord a new song' (Psalm 96:1). This is literally true of this edition. As Editorial Consultant Dr. Erik Routley explains in his preface, an attempt has been made to produce a new kind of hymn book with songs and hymns from all the main streams of the Church—Orthodox, Roman Catholic and Protestant—and from a wide variety of cultures. This hymn book has also the great merit of expressing the faith and aspirations of people in modern idiom and in terms of their real concerns today.

Special thanks are due to Dr. Routley and his team of editors for the mastery with which they have accomplished their extremely difficult but exciting task. The Melody edition, which appeared in 1974, was published by Bärenreiter-Verlag, Kassel, and has been and is being widely used. We are delighted to present finally the Music edition, produced by Oxford University Press. We hope that the Music edition will ensure increasing and even more effective use of this new ecumenical hymn book. While most of the hymns in the Melody edition have been printed in two or more languages, this Music edition is confined, for space reasons, to two languages—the original, and English translation where this is needed. The Melody edition will, therefore, be of continuing value for singing in different countries. We would express our deep gratitude to Doreen Potter, who since 1967 undertook the preliminary task of preparing for the revision of the old Cantate Domino, and has unsparingly laboured to see this new edition through the press.

We now have an instrument whereby we can joyfully fulfil that other call of the Psalmist: 'Sing to the Lord, all the earth' (Psalm 96:2).

Geneva
Advent, 1979

Philip Potter
General Secretary
World Council of Churches

Editor's Introduction

'How will Christians of the future sing? As members of the universal Church, or not at all.' That was said at one of the editoral consultations which led to the making of this book; and it could be regarded as the book's governing principle. It is with such a sentiment as that in mind that we now offer it to Christians of all races and opinions, so that we may all share each other's praises.

History of the Book. Cantate Domino was first published in 1924 as a book of 64 hymns taken from many national sources, each appearing in several languages. In 1930 a revised edition, with 82 hymns in 23 languages, was published and in 1951 a further revision appeared, containing 120 hymns. All these were published by the World Student Christian Federation in Geneva.

The present book is therefore the fourth edition of *Cantate Domino*, but it is much more than a revision of the third. It reflects radical changes of policy and outlook which themselves reflect the needs of a new age.

In the first place, the book has been prepared by a special committee convened by the World Council of Churches. In the second, it is nearly twice the size of the third edition, with a much wider coverage of cultures, styles and languages. In the third place, there has been active participation in its editing from within the Roman Catholic and Orthodox churches.

The Making of the Book. In December 1968 a meeting was called by the World Council of Churches in Geneva to explore the question whether a new *Cantate Domino* was practicable. As a consequence of this working parties were organized in several national centres and a list of some 200 correspondents was compiled; these were approached for material and advice. In May 1970 a consultative committee met in the Russian Orthodox House in the Rue Beaumont, Geneva, to report on the first stages of progress. There an editorial board was appointed. This consisted of Fr Joseph Gelineau, Professor Dimitri Stefanovic, Propst Dr. Dieter Trautwein and Mr Erich Weingärtner, who represented respectively the Roman Catholic, Orthodox, European Protestant and American Lutheran traditions, with Dr. Erik Routley as General Editorial Consultant and chairman of the board. To these were added, from among those permanently in

Geneva, Dr. Konrad Raiser, staff member of the Faith and Order Secretariat especially charged with responsibility for the project, Mrs Doreen Potter, wife of Philip Potter, herself a composer with special interest in contemporary hymns, the Reverend Fred Kaan of the staff of the World Alliance of Reformed Churches and a celebrated hymnwriter, and, until April 1972, Miss Margot Toplis. Miss Toplis, who was appointed to take special responsibility for the secretarial work, left for other work in April 1972, and Mr Weingärtner moved out of direct involvement in the Board's work when he finished his period of service with the Lutheran World Federation in the same year. When Miss Toplis left Geneva her secretarial work was taken over by Miss Sally Woolston, and at a later stage Mrs Potter gave substantial assistance with the preparation of the fair copy for the publisher. This is an appropriate place to thank these three especially for their very great contribution to the work which is now in the reader's hands.

We also gratefully acknowledge here the support given to the World Council in this project by several member churches. Financial contributions were made in particular by churches in the Federal Republic of Germany, Sweden, the USA and the Netherlands. The Evangelical Lutheran Church in Finland made a most welcome gift of paper.

It was the task of this editorial Board to gather together the findings of the various working parties and to prepare the manuscript of the book. A consultation in June 1971 made a first attempt to find a way through the enormous mass of material that already lay before us. The Board met again in October 1971 with certain invited guests, including Bishop F. Pagura, formerly of Panama and Costa Rica, and Fr Christopher Coelho of India (some of whose work is in this book), and a new draft of the book was prepared. After much correspondence, a final meeting of the Board was held in October 1972. During this consultative period eight separate drafts of the book were assembled, and the last of these was abridged at a late stage on the publisher's advice; this is what you now have in your hand. The editors are deeply grateful to the publishers, Bärenreiter-Verlag, not only for their readiness to invest in such an unusual book but also for the open-hearted collaboration they have brought to so many of the awkward details.

The Purpose of the Book. At an early stage it was agreed that the purpose of the book was to serve the church at its 'growing points'. The Church is at present growing, we believe, through the meeting of cultures and races, as well as through experiments in text-writing, music and liturgy; an international hymn book with an experimental emphasis was clearly called for, and we have sought to include in the book material in many styles. Not only hymns of the familiar kind will be found here, but also antiphonal canticles and folk songs. We hope to make available not only the hymnody of the west to the east, and of the north to the south, as did the older missionary enterprises, but some of the new and vital hymnody of the southern hemisphere to the north, and of the east to the west.

Translations. This has meant that we have had to be much more flexible in our use of translations than were the earlier editors. On the one hand, it is not now felt to be so necessary that members of an international congregation should sing each in his own language: on the other hand, it has been found that not all our material can be satisfactorily translated into a standard number of languages. So we do not now present all the material in English, French and German, as in the earlier editions. The principle has been to present everything in its original language and in English (although even this we have not followed pedantically), and in such other languages as seemed to carry it best. A few hymns appear in one language only; while a small number of the more familiar classics are given in up to eight languages.

To avoid, however, undue difficulty of presentation, we have retained the tradition of using French, German and English as the basic languages for translation. In each of these language areas a panel of translators has chosen hymns to be translated, and has made or selected the versions we now present. In certain cases, especially in the French versions, we were quite content that the versions should emerge as paraphrases: in one or two cases, indeed, they are new compositions which have nothing but the melody in common with the originals. In such cases, and where there is a different number of stanzas in the different versions, we have indicated that it would be inadvisable to sing these versions concurrently with the originals.

The Use of the Book. You have, then, a quite new kind of hymn book in your hand. It is not the first multilingual book to appear, but it is different from its contemporaries and predecessors to an extent that makes it necessary to recommend some care in its use.

We envisage its use in two ways. On the one hand it is, we feel, uniquely appropriate to international gatherings, large or small. It will find a natural place in any conference centre, retreat house, tourist centre, ocean liner, or other meeting place where people of different languages and cultures gather. But also—especially perhaps in areas where French, German or English are major languages—it can be used as a supplement to a parish hymnal, or to that of a university chapel or a school, in order to enrich the religious experience of those who use it in exactly those directions in which the Church is growing most energetically at present.

In either case, much of the contents will be unfamiliar. Many of the texts and tunes we have selected are unknown outside the communities which have used them up to now; some are altogether new. We offer songs in styles that encourage accompaniment on other instruments than the pianoforte or organ, and songs that invite antiphonal treatment. Whatever its context, we urge that the use of the book be assisted, and usually preceded, by its informal use for practice and for the improvement of people's acquaintance with its various styles. Do not confine yourself to the five or six hymns in it with which you are already familiar. Use whatever talents are available to teach, from the beginning, those new pieces, and thus to introduce those new ecumenical experiences, which only this book makes available in a single collection.

We commend this book to all Christians who care to make use of it. For us, the editorial board and consultants, it is a celebration of that friendship between the nations, and between the different Christian bodies, which the World Council of Churches was founded to promote, and for which our Faith requires us constantly to work and pray. It is, in itself, no more than a chapter in a much longer story, a stage in a long, arduous and rewarding pilgrimage. But such as it is, it represents our effort to serve the churches which we love, and the Lord under whose judgement and promise we all stand.

For the Editorial Board,
ERIK ROUTLEY

Newcastle upon Tyne, England
St Andrew's Day 1973

Acknowledgements · Dankesbezeigung
Remerciements

We wish to thank all those who have granted permission for the use of material in this book. We have made every effort to trace and identify copyright holders and to request all the necessary permission for reprinting. But in some cases this proved impossible and in others no reply has been received. If we have erred in any way in the acknowledgements or have unwittingly infringed any copyright, we apologize sincerely, and shall be glad to make the necessary corrections in subsequent editions.

Wir möchten allen danken, die die Genehmigung zum Abdruck von Quellenmaterial in diesem Buch erteilt haben. Wir haben uns nach bestem Wissen und Gewissen bemüht, die jeweiligen Urheber festzustellen und die erforderliche Genehmigung zum Nachdruck einzuholen. Dies ist uns jedoch in einigen Fällen nicht möglich gewesen, in anderen haben wir keine Antwort erhalten. Sollte uns in den Hinweisen ein Fehler unterlaufen sein oder sollten wir unwissentlich gegen ein Copyright verstossen haben, so bitten wir um Entschuldigung. Wir werden solche Fehler selbstverständlich bei allen Neuauflagen korrigieren.

Nous tenons à remercier tous ceux qui nous ont autorisés à reproduire leurs œuvres dans le présent ouvrage. Nous avons fait tout notre possible pour retrouver les titulaires de droits d'auteur et leur demander une autorisation de reproduction. Cependant dans certains cas, nos recherches n'ont pas abouti, et dans d'autres, nos requêtes sont restées sans réponse. Si par inadvertance, nous avons omis d'exprimer des remerciements à qui de droit, ou enfreint des droits d'auteur, nous nous en excusons très sincèrement et serons heureux de pouvoir réparer cette omission dans les éditions ultérieures.

Abbreviations / Abkürzungen / Abréviations

Arr. = Arranged by
Harm. = Harmonised by
Harm. C.D. = Harmonised Cantate Domino
M: Melody / Melodie / Melodie
O: Original / Original / Original
Q: Sources / Quellen / Sources
T: Text / Text / Texte

Languages / Sprachen / Langues

d	= German / deutsch / allemand
e	= English / englisch / anglais
f	= French / französisch / français
fin	= Finnish / finnisch / finnois
nie	= Dutch / niederländisch / néerlandais
no	= Norwegian / norwegisch / norvégien
p	= Portuguese / portugiesisch / portugais
s	= Spanish / spanisch / espagnol
schw	= Swedish / schwedisch / suédois
su	= Swahili / suaheli / swahili
tsch	= Czech / tschechisch / tchêque
un	= Hungarian / ungarisch / hongrois
yor	= Yoriba / Yoruba / yoruba

Publishers / Verlage / Editeurs

CNPL	= Centre National Pastorale Liturgique, Paris
SEFIM	= Secrétariat des Editeurs de Fiches Musicales, Paris
Grail	= Grail Publications, Nottingham

Hymn No.	Writer, Translator/Composer, Arranger	Copyright Holder or Controller	Source
1	T: (O: f) Roger Chapal (e) William Kethe. M: *Octante-trois Pseaumes*, Geneva, 1551. Harm. C. Goudimel 1562	T: (f) Centre National Pastorale Liturgique, Paris	T: (f) Cantate Domino III
2	T: (O: e) Isaac Watts. M: William Croft 1708		
3	T: (O: e) John Milton. M: China, Buddhist Temple chant		
4	T: (O: f) Roger Chapal (e) Erik Routley. M: *Octante-trois Pseaumes*, Geneva, 1551. Harm. Cantate Domino	T: (f) Fédération Protestante de France (Musique et chant), Paris (e) E. Routley	T: (e) Cantate Domino III
5	T: (O: f) Roger Chapal (e) Robert Bridges. M: *Pseaulmes cinquante de David*, Lyon, 1547. Harm. C. Goudimel 1562	T: (f) Fédération Protestante de France (Musique et chant), Paris (e) Oxford University Press, London	T: (e) *Yattendon Hymnal*
6	T: (O: f) Roger Chapal (e) Erik Routley. M: *Octante-trois Pseaumes*, Geneva, 1551. Harm. John Wilson 1964	T: (f) Fédération Protestante de France (Musique et chant) Paris (e) 1974 Agape, Carol Stream, Illinois 60187, USA. International copyright secured. Used by permission	T: (e) *Ecumenical Praise*
7	T: (O: thai) C. Kingshill (e) Erik Routley. M: Thai traditional melody.	T: (thai) Christian Literature Department of the Church of Christ in Thailand (e) + M	(thai) Thai Hymnal (e) *Westminster Praise*

Hymn No.	Writer, Translator/Composer, Arranger	Copyright Holder or Controller	Source
	Arr. Erik Routley	arr. 1976 Hinshaw Music Inc., P.O. Box 470, Chapel Hill, N.C., USA	
8	T: (O: e) Fred Kaan. M: Margot Toplis	T: (e) 1976 Stainer & Bell Ltd., London. M: Margot Toplis	T: (e) *Pilgrim Praise* M: Cantate Domino III
9	T: (O: fin) Julius Krohn (e) E. E. Ryden/Toivo Harjunpää. M: Finnish traditional melody. Harm. Cantate Domino	T: (e) Lutheran World Federation, Geneva	T: (e) *Laudamus*
10	T: (O: d) Gerhard Valentin (e) Emily Chisholm. M: and Arr. Rolf Schweizer	M + T: (d,e) Hänssler-Verlag, Neuhausen-Stuttgart 1964	M + T(d) *Bausteine für den Gottesdienst* (HE 19.403) (e) Cantate Domino III
11	T: (O: malagasy) Psalm 102(103) (e) U.S. Leupold. M: Malagasy melody 1818. Harm. Cantate Domino	T: (e) Lutheran World Federation, Geneva	T: (e) *Laudamus*
12	T: (O: e) Barry Chevannes. M: Barry Chevannes. Harm. Cantate Domino	M + T: (e) Barry Chevannes	Manuscript collection by Barry Chevannes
13	T: (O: e) Psalm 112(113)/ Marjorie Jillson (d) Heinz Werner Zimmermann	M + T: (e,d) Concordia Publishing House, St Louis, Missouri, USA, 1973. Used with permission	M + T: (e) *Five Hymns*
14	T: (O: e) Ewald Bash. M: Latvian traditional melody. Arr. John Ylvisaker. Harm. Cantate Domino	M + Arr. + T(e) American Lutheran Church, Youth Department, Minneapolis, USA. Harm. Erik Routley	M + T(e) *Songs for Today*
15	T: (O: e) Brian Foley. M: Elizabeth Poston	M + T(e) Faber Music Ltd., London	M + T(e) *New Catholic Hymnal*
16	T: (O: d) Psalm 91(92) (e) Ivor Jones. M: Rolf Schweizer	M + T: (d,e,) 1966, Hänssler-Verlag, Neuhausen-Stuttgart	M + T(d) *Neue Lieder, Beigleitsätze für Tasten-instrumente* (HE 19.508) (e) Cantate Domino III
17	T: (O: d) Psalm 107(108) (e) Ivor Jones. M + Setting: Paul Ernst Ruppel	M + T: (d) Verlag Singende Gemeinde, Wuppertal. CS 85376 (e) Ivor Jones, London	M + T: (d) *Singheft* 1976 (e) Cantate Domino III
18	T: (O: e) E. Mawelera Tembo. M: Traditional Malawi wedding song. Arr. Cantate Domino	M + T(e) The Overton Institution, Livingstonian Mission, Malawi	M + T(e) *Africa Praise*
19	T: (f) from Psalm 8. Antienne: M + T(f) J. Samson, Psalmodie: M + T(f) J. Gelineau	M + T(f) Editions du Cerf, Paris	M + T(f) *Vingt-quatre Psaumes et un cantique*
20	T: (O: f) de la bible de Jérusalem. Antienne: M + T(f) J. Samson, Psalmodie: M + T(f) J. Gelineau	M: Z 22 Cerf (SEFIM)	M + T(f) *Vingt-quatre Psaumes et un cantique*

Hymn No.	Writer, Translator/Composer, Arranger	Copyright Holder or Controller	Source
21	T: (O: f) from Psalm 23(24). Antienne + Psalmodie: J. Gelineau (M+T)	M: Z 23 Cerf (SEFIM, Paris)	*Vingt-quatre Psaumes et un cantique*
22	T: (e) Psalm 118(119). M: Christopher Coelho	T(e) The Grail, England. M: Christopher Coelho	T: (e) The Grail Translation
23	T: (e) Psalm 24(25). M: Christopher Coelho	T: (e) The Grail, England. M: Christopher Coelho	T: (e) The Grail Translation
24	T: (O: f) from Psalm 102(103). Antienne: M+T(f) J. Langlais/ Psalmodie: J. Gelineau (e) The Grail	T: (e) The Grail, England. M: Z 102 Cerf (SEFIM, Paris)	T: (e) The Grail Translation. M: *Cinquante-trois Psaumes et quatre cantiques*
25	T: (O: f) Joseph Samson (e) The Psalms—Erik Routley. M: Joseph Samson	M+T(f) Editions du Cerf, Paris (e) Erik Routley	T: (e) The Psalms, a version for singing
26	T: (O: f) from Psalm 129(130). Antienne: J. Gelineau (e) The Grail. M: J. Gelineau	M: SEFIM, Paris	*Ving-quatre Psaumes et un cantique*
27	T: (O: f) from Psalm 135(136). M: J. Gelineau (e) The Grail	M: Z 135 Cerf (SEFIM, Paris)	*Vingt-quatre Psaumes et un cantique*
28	T: (O-tamil) Psalm 150 (e) Erik Routley. M: Charles Mani	T: (e) Erik Routley. M: Charles Mani, O.F.M.	
29	T: (O: e) Harry Emerson Fosdick. M: Henry Purcell	T: (e) Dr Elinor Fosdick Downs, New York	
30	T: (O: e) Nick Hodson. M: Nick Hodson. Harm. Erik Routley	M+T: (e) The Liturgical Conference, USA. Harm. Erik Routley	
31	T: (O: e) John Hoad. M: Doreen Potter	T: (e) John Hoad. M: 1974 Agape, Carol Stream, Illinois 60187, USA. International Copyright secured. Used by permission.	Cantate Domino III
32	T: (O: d) Christa Weiss (e) John B. Geyer. M: Hans-Rudolf Siemoneit	T: (d) Bosse Edition, Regensburg (e) John B. Geyer. M: Gütersloher Verlagshaus, Gütersloh	M+T(d) *Neue geistliche Lieder*
33	T: (O: schw) Anders Frostenson (e) Fred Kaan. M: Sven-Eric Johanson	T: (O: schw) Anders Frostenson (e) 1976 Stainer & Bell Ltd., London. M: Verbum, Stockholm	M+T(schw) *71 psalmer och visor*, Verbum, Stockholm (e) Cantate Domino III
34	T: (O: e) John Ferguson. M: Reginald Barrett-Ayres	M+T(e) 1976 Stainer & Bell Ltd., London	M+T(e) *Dunblane Praises*
35	T: (O: p) João Dias de Araujo (e) Fred Kaan. M: J. W. Faustini	T: (e) Fred Kaan. M: J. W. Faustini	M+T(p) Os Céus Proclmam (e) Cantate Domino III
36	T: (O: e) S. Wilfred Hodge. M: Doreen Potter	T: (e) S. Wilfred Hodge. M: Doreen Potter	Cantate Domino III

Hymn No.	Writer, Translator/Composer, Arranger	Copyright Holder or Controller	Source
37	T: (O: e) Sydney Carter. M: Sydney Carter. Harm. Cantate Domino	M + T(e) 1976 Stainer & Bell Ltd., London	Celebration series
38	T: (O: e) Fred Kaan. M: Doreen Potter	M + T(e) 1976 Stainer & Bell Ltd., London	*Pilgrim Praise*
39	T: (O: e) Fred Kaan. M: Doreen Potter	M + T(e) 1976 Stainer & Bell Ltd., London	*Pilgrim Praise*
40	(a) T: (O: e) Erik Routley. M: Philibert Jambe-de-Fer	T: (e) 1976 Stainer & Bell Ltd., London	*Dunblane Praises II*
	(b) T: (O: e) Erik Routley. M. Peter Cutts	T: (e) 1976 Stainer & Bell Ltd., London. M: Oxford University Press, London	T: (e) *Dunblane Praises*
41	T: (O: e) G. K. Chesterton. M: English traditional. Harm. R. Vaughan Williams	T: (e) Oxford University Press, London	
42	T: (O: e) Clifford Bax. M: *Octante-trois Pseaumes*, Geneva, 1551. English form of melody. Harm. W. Parsons	T: (e) D. Peters & Co., London	M + T(e) *Songs of Praise*
43	T: (O: e) Fred Kaan. M: Geoffrey Laycock	M: Faber Music, London. T: (e) 1976 Stainer & Bell Ltd., London	M + T(e) *New Catholic Hymnal*
44	T: (O: schw) Anders Frostenson (e) Fred Kaan. M: Gustaf Bjarnegård	M: Verbum, Stockholm. T: (schw) Anders Frostenson (e) 1976 Stainer & Bell Ltd., London	M + T(schw) *Psalmer och visor 76*, Verbum, Stockholm (e) Cantate Domino III
45	T: (O: e) Fred Kaan. M: Erik Routley	T: (e) 1976 Stainer & Bell Ltd., London. M: 1974 Agape, Carol Stream, Illinois 60187, USA. International copyright secured. Used by permission.	M + T: (e) *Pilgrim Praise*
46	T: (O: f) Didier Rimaud (e) Caryl Micklem. M: Joseph Gelineau	T: (e) Caryl Micklem (f) P 81 Centre National Pastorale Liturgique, Paris. M: Studio SM	
47	T: (O: d) Paulus Stein (e) F. Pratt Green. M: and Arr. Rolf Schweizer	M + T: (d,e) 1963 Hänssler Verlag, Neuhausen-Stuttgart	M + T: (d) 1963 *Bausteine für den Gottesdienst* (HE 19401) (e) Cantate Domino III
48	T: (O: d) Dietrich Bonhoeffer (e) F. Pratt Green. M: Joseph Gelineau	T: (d) Chr. Kaiser Verlag, München (e) Oxford University Press, London. M: SEFIM, Paris	M + T(e) Cantate Domino III (d) aus: Dietrich Bonhoeffer, "Widerstand und Ergebung", Chr. Kaiser Verlag, München. Neueausgabe 1970, S. 435 f.
49	T: (O: schw) Anders Frostenson (e) Fred Kaan. M: Lars Åke Lundberg	M: Verbum, Stockholm. T: (schw) Anders Frostenson (e) 1976 Stainer & Bell Ltd., London	M + T: (schw) *Psalmer och visor 76*, Verbum, Stockholm (e) Cantate Domino III

xvii

Hymn No.	Writer, Translator/Composer, Arranger	Copyright Holder or Controller	Source
50	T: (O: e) Fred Kaan. M: James Carley	M + T(e) 1976 Stainer & Bell Ltd., London	M + T(e) *Pilgrim Praise*
51	T: (O: nie) W. Barnard (e) Fred Kaan. M: Frits Mehrtens	M + T(nie) Interkerklijke Stichting voor het Kerklied, Pijnacker, Holland (e) Fred Kaan	M + T(nie) *Liedbook voor de Kerken* (e) Cantate Domino III
52	T: (O: nie) Huub Oosterhuis (e) Redmond McGoldrick. M: B. Huijbers	M + T(nie) Gooi en Sticht, Hilversum, Holland (e) North American Liturgy Resources, Phoenix, Arizona, USA	M + T: (nie) *Liturgischen Gezangen* (e) *Prayers, Poems and Songs*
53	T: (O: lat) (e) J. M. Neale. M: French melody		
54	T: (O: f) Dominique Ombrie (e) F. Pratt Green. M: Dominique Ombrie	T(f) E 34. M: Chalet (SEFIM, Paris) (e) Oxford University Press, London	T: (e) Cantate Domino III
55	T: (O: e) Walter Russell Bowie. M: Ludwig Lindemann	T(e) Abingdon Press, Nashville, Tennessee, USA	M + T(e) *Hymns for Church and School*
56	T: (O: d) Jochen Klepper (e) F. Pratt Green. M: Johannes Petzold	M + T(d) Bärenreiter-Verlag, Kassel, Tours, London (e) Oxford University Press, London	M + T(d) *Neue Weihnachtslieder* (e) Cantate Domino III
57	T: (O: s) F. J. Pagura (e) F. Pratt Green. M: Homero Perera	M + T(s) Methopress (h. La Aurora) (e) Oxford University Press	M + T(s) *Cantico Nuevo* (e) Cantate Domino III
58	T: (O: lat) Prudentius (e) R. F. Davis. M: *Piae Cantiones.* Harm. *Church Hymnary*		
59	T: (O: e) Malcom Stewart. M: Malcom Stewart	M + T(e) 1976 Stainer & Bell Ltd., London	M + T(e) *Gospel Songs for Today*
60	T: (O: d) Dieter Trautwein (e) Fred Kaan. M: Gottfried Neubert und Seminargruppe, Frankfurt. Harm. Herbert Beuerle	M + T(d) Burckhardthaus-Verlag, Gelnhausen (e) Fred Kaan	M + T(d) *Schalom* (e) Cantate Domino III
61	T: (O: d) Kurt Rommel (e) Emily Chisholm. M: Gerd Watkinson. Harm. Cantate Domino	M + T(d) Burckhardthaus-Verlag, Gelnhausen (e) Emily Chisholm	M + T(d) *Schalom* (e) Cantate Domino III
62	T: (O: e) D. T. Niles. M: Maluka popular tune. Harm. Cantate Domino	T(e) P. Niles, Princeton	*East Asia Hymnal*
63	T: (O: f) Didier Rimaud (e) F. Pratt Green. M: C. Geoffray. Harm. J. Bonfils	T: (f) F 47 éd. du Seuil (e) Oxford University Press, London	M: *Cantiques et psaumes.* T(e) Cantate Domino III
64	T: (O: f) Claude Rozier (e) F. Pratt Green. M: traditionelle d'Auvergne. Harm. M. E. Rose	M + T(f) Editions du Cerf, Paris (e) Oxford University Press, London	M: *Cantiques et Psaumes.* T(e,f) Cantate Domino III

Hymn No.	Writer, Translator/Composer, Arranger	Copyright Holder or Controller	Source
65	T: (O: lat) (e) F. Oakeley. M: J. F. Wade. Harm. Cantate Domino		Cantate Domino II
66	T: (O: d) Dieter Trautwein/Kurt Rommel (e) F. Pratt Green. M: Dieter Trautwein. Harm. Hans Rudolf Siemoneit	M + T(d) Burckhardthaus-Verlag, Gelnhausen (e) Oxford University Press, London	M + T(d) *Schalom* (e) Cantate Domino III
67	T: (O: fin) Juhani Forsberg (e) Emily Chisholm. M: Juhani Forsberg	M + T(fin) Juhani Forsberg (e) Emily Chisholm	T: (e) Cantate Domino
68	T: (O: e) Psalm. M: William Llewellyn	M: Oxford University Press, London	M + T(e) *Hymns for Celebration*
69	T: (O: schw) Anders Frostenson (e) Fred Kaan. M: Roland Forsberg	T: (schw) Anders Frostenson (e) 1976 Stainer & Bell Ltd., London. M: Verbum, Stockholm	M + T(schw) *Psalmer och visor* 76, Verbum Stockholm (e) Cantate Domino III
70	T: (O: hindi) Bantam Ram Banda (e) Erik Routley. M: Staff notation R. Patterson	T: (e) Erik Routley	M + T(hindi) *Masihi Sangeet* (e) Cantate Domino III
71	T: (O: e) Fred Kaan. M: Sri Lanka. Harm. Cantate Domino	T: (e) Fred Kaan	M + T(e) *New Songs of Asian Cities*
72	T: (O: schw) Anders Frostenson (e) Fred Kaan. M: Carl Nielsen	T: (O: schw) Anders Frostenson (e) 1976 Stainer & Bell Ltd., London. M: Edition Wilhelm Hansen, Copenhagen	M + T(schw) *Psalmer och visor* 76, Verbum, Stockholm (e) Cantate Domino III
73	T: (O: d) Dieter Trautwein (e) F. Pratt Green. M: Gerhard Kloft	M + T(d) Burckhardthaus-Verlag, Gelnhausen (e) Oxford University Press, London	M + T(d) *Schalom* (e) Cantate Domino III
74	T: (O: nie) Huub Oosterhuis (e) R. McGoldrick. M: Tera de Marez Oyens	M + T(nie) Interkerkelijke Stichting voor het Kerklied	M + T(nie) *Liedboek voor de Kerken* (e) Cantate Domino III
75	T: (O: e) 1 Cor. 13/John 15. M: J. B. Fernandes	M: J. B. Fernandes	
76	T: (O: p) John 13 (e) Helena Scott. M: José Alves	T: (e) Helena Scott. M: José Alves	
77	T: (O: p) John 15 (e) Helena Scott. M: José Weber	T: (e) Helena Scott. M: José Weber	
78	T: (O: f) Didier Rimaud (e) F. Pratt Green. M: Joseph Gelineau	T(f) + M: H 67/1 Levain CNPL (SEFIM, Paris) (e) Oxford University Press, London	T(e) Cantate Domino III
79	T: (O: e) American Folk Hymn. M: Melody from *Southern Harmony* 1835. Harm. Cantate Domino		

Hymn No.	Writer, Translator/Composer, Arranger	Copyright Holder or Controller	Source
80	T: (O: e) S. Crossman. M: John Ireland	M: Dr John Ireland (Norah Kirby, Steyning)	
81	T: (O: schw) Anders Frostenson (e) Fred Kaan. M: Verner Ahlberg	T: (schw) Anders Frostenson (e) 1976 Stainer & Bell Ltd., London. M: Verbum, Stockholm	M + T(schw) *Psalmer och visor* 76, Verbum, Stockholm (e) Cantate Domino III
82(a)	T: (O: d) Paul Gerhardt (e) J. W. Alexander. M: Hans Leo Hassler. Harm. Cantate Domino		*Evangelisches Kirchengesangbuch*
(b)	Harm. J. S. Bach		
83	T: (O: e) Isaac Watts. M: Edward Miller		
84	T: (O: d) Michael Weisse (e) C. A. Alington. M: Melchior Vulpius. Harm. F. Layriz	T: (e) By permission of Hymns Ancient & Modern Ltd., Worthing	T(e) Cantate Domino III
85	M + T(O: e) Negro Spiritual edited by John W. Work		M + T(e) *American Negro Songs and Spirituals*
86	T: (O: f) Abel Nkuinji (e) Erik Routley. M: Traditional melody from Cameroon. Harm. Cantate Domino	T: (f) Abel Nkuinji (e) 1972 Agape, Carol Stream, Illinois 60187, USA. International copyright secured. Used by permission	T: (e) *Ecumenical Praise*
87	T: (O: su) Joas Kijugo (e) Erik Routley. M: Joas Kijugo	M + T(su) Joas Kijugo (e) Erik Routley	T: (e) Cantate Domino III
88	T: (O: su) Bernard Kyamanywa (e) Howard S. Olson. M: Tanzanian traditional melody Harm. Cantate Domino	M + T(su,e) Lutheran World Federation, Geneva	*Laudamus*
89	T: (O: s) Nicolas Martinez (e) Fred Kaan. M: Pablo D. Sosa. Harm. Cantate Domino	M + T(s) Metho Press Ltd., Buenos Aires (e) Fred Kaan	M + T(s) Cantico Nuevo (e) Cantate Domino III
90	T: (O: persisch) Hasson Dehqani-Tafti (e) Lewis M. Johnson. M: Persian melody. Harm. Cantate Domino	T(persisch) Hasson Dehqani-Tafti	M + T(persisch) *Persian Hymnbook* (e) Cantate Domino III
91	T: (O: d) 13. Jahrh. (e) E. Miles Coverdale. M. 13. Jahrh.		M + T(d) *Evangelisches Kirchengesangbuch*
92	T: (O: d) Martin Luther (e) R. Massie. M: Martin Luther. Harm. Cantate Domino		M + T(d) *Evangelisches Gesangbuch*
93	T: (O: f) Edmund Budry (e) F. Pratt Green. M: George Frederick Handel	T(f) World Council of Churches, Geneva (e) Oxford University Press, London	Cantate Domino I
94	T: (O: e) Charles Wesley. M: *Lyra Davidica* (1741). Harm. *Hymns Ancient and Modern* (1861)		

Hymn No.	Writer, Translator/Composer, Arranger	Copyright Holder or Controller	Source
95	T: (O: e) John B. Geyer. M: Charles Villiers Stanford	T: (e) John B. Geyer. M: 1976 Stainer & Bell Ltd., London	
96	T: (O: f) Didier Rimaud (e) Brian Wren (Refrain by Sir Ronald Johnson). M: Jean Langlais	M+T(f) F 64 (SEFIM, Paris) (e) Oxford University Press, London	
97	T: (O: e) F. Pratt Green. M: *Paris Antiphoner*. Harm. Cantate Domino	T:(e) Oxford University Press, London	
98	T: (O: f) Dominique Ombrie (e) Erik Routley. M: Dominique Ombrie	M+T(f) D 86 Chalet (SEFIM, Paris) (e) Erik Routley	
99	T: (O: e) Isaac Watts. M: *Psalmodia Evangelica* 1789. Harm. *English Hymnal* 1906		
100(a)	T: (O: lat) 9th Century (e) Robert Bridges. M: Vatican Plainsong melody, Mode vii	T: (e) Oxford University Press, London	T(e) *Yattendon Hymnal*
(b)	M: Reformation form of melody. Harm. Cantate Domino		
101	T: (O: d) Martin Luther (e) Fred Kaan. M: Latter form of melody in *Encheiridion* 1524. Harm. Cantate Domino	T: (e) 1976 Stainer & Bell Ltd., London	M+T(d) *Evangelischeskirchen Gesangbuch*
102	T: tr. (e) R. F. Littledale. M: Ralph Vaughan Williams	T: (e) Non-copyright. M: Oxford University Press, London	M: *English Hymnal*
103	T: (O: d) Dieter Trautwein (e) F. Pratt Green. M: H. R. Siemoneit	T: (d) Burckhardthaus-Verlag, Gelnhausen. M: Gütersloher Verlagshaus, Gütersloh (e) Oxford University Press, London	M+T(d) *Schalom* (e) Cantate Domino
104	T: (O: e) A. M. Jones. M: Yoruba tune. *Fela Sowande* 1969	T: (e) Lutterworth Press, Guildford, England	M+T(e) *Africa Praise*
105	T: (O: f) Didier Rimaud (e) Erik Routley. M: Jean van der Cauter	M+T(f) SEFIM, Paris (e) 1972 Agape, Carol Stream, Illinois 60187, USA. International copyright secured. Used by permission.	T: (e) *Ecumenical Praise*
106	T: (O: japanese) Saichiro Yuya (e) Esther Hibbard. M: Traditional Japanese melody. Harm. Toraji Ōnaka	M+T(e) Church of Christ, Tokyo	M+T(e) *Hymns of the Church*
107	T: (O: f) Claude Rozier (e) F. Pratt Green. M: Erik Routley	T: (f) SEFIM (e) Oxford University Press, London. M: Hinshaw Inc., 1979	T: (e) Cantate Domino III

Hymn No.	Writer, Translator/Composer, Arranger	Copyright Holder or Controller	Source
108	T: (O: d) Joachim Neander (e) Catherine Winkworth. M: *Stralsund Gesangbuch* 1665		
109	T: (O: e) Isaac Watts. M: from *Kölner Gesangbuch* 1623. Harm. Ralph Vaughan Williams 1906		
110	T: (O: d) Martin Rinkhardt (e) Catherine Winkworth. M: Johann Crüger 1636. Harm. Cantate Domino		
111	T: (O: lat) St Francis of Assisi (e) W. H. Draper. M: from *Kölner Gesangbuch* 1623. Harm. Ralph Vaughan Williams 1906	M: Oxford University Press, London. Harm. RVW Ltd., London. T: (e) Curwen Edition, London	Cantate Domino II
112	M + T(f) Abel Nkuinji 1970. Harm. Cantate Domino	M + T(f) Abel Nkuinji	*Chantons*, Caméroun
113	T: (O: d) Psalm 148/Jörg Zink/ Dieter Hechtenberg (e) Emily Chisholm. M: Dieter Hechtenberg	M + T(d,e) Christophorus- Verlag Herder, Freiburg	*111 Kinderlieder zur Bible*
114	T: (O: japanese) Tokuo Yamaguchi (e) E. M. Stowe. M: Isao Koizumi 1958	M + T(japanese) Church of Christ, Tokyo (e) Lutheran World Federation, Geneva	T: (e) *Laudamus*
115	T: (O: no) Petter Dass (e) Eivind Berggrav. M: Norwegian folk song. Harm. Cantate Domino	M + T(e,no) Lutheran World Federation, Geneva	M + T(no,e) *Laudamus*
116	T: (O: e) Timothy Rees. M: Herbert Murill 1951	M + T(e) Mowbrays & Co. Ltd., Oxford	M + T(e) *The Mirfield Mission Hymnbook*
117	T: (O: yor) Olajida Olude (e) Biodun Adebesin/Austin Lovelace. M: Olajida Olude. Harm. Cantate Domino	M + T(yor) Olajida Olude	M + T(yor) *Yoruba Hymns and Carols*
118	T: (O: e) Fred Kaan. M: Sri Lanka traditional melody	T: (e) Fred Kaan	M + T(e) *New Songs of Asian Cities*
119	T: (O: d) N. Decius (e) Catherine Winkworth. M: N. Decius. Harm. Cantate Domino		
120	T: (O: tsch) Jiří Zábójnik (e) J. J. Vajda. M: from *Paris Antiphoner* 1681. Harm. Erik Routley	T(e) Lutheran World Federation, Geneva. Harm. Erik Routley	T(e) *Laudamus*
121	T: (O: e) D. T. Niles. M: Elena G. Maquiso. Harm. Cantate Domino	T: (e) P. Niles, Princeton	M + T(e) *EACC Hymnal*
122	T: (O: d) Martin Luther (e) Erik Routley. M: Medieval church melody arr. Martin Luther 1524. Harm. Cantate Domino	T: (e) 1976 Hinshaw Music Inc.	M + T(d) Cantate Domino II (e) *Westminster Praise*

Hymn No.	Writer, Translator/Composer, Arranger	Copyright Holder or Controller	Source
123	T: (O: e) Mary Byrne. M: Traditional Irish melody. Harm. Erik Routley	T: (e) Chatto & Windus Ltd., London	T: (e) An altered version from the 1951 *BBC Hymn Book* of 'A Prayer' (Be Thou My Vision) from *The Poem Book of the Gael*: selected and edited by Eleanor Hull.
124	T: (O: chinese) T. C. Chao (e) Frank W. Price. M: Traditional Chinese melody. Harm. Cantate Domino	T: (e) Dr Frank W. Price, Lexington	M + T(chinese) P'u Tien Sung Tsan (e) *EACC Hymnal*.
125	T: (O: japanese) Sogo Matsumoto (e) Esther Hibbard. M: 12th century traditional Japanese melody. Harm. Isao Koizumi	T: (japanese) Church of Christ, Tokyo	T: (japanese) Sanbika 1955
126	T: (O: d) J. W. Franck (e) Catherine Winkworth. M: Johann Crüger. Harm. Cantate Domino		
127	T: (O: d) Schalom Ben-Chorim (e) Ivor Jones. M: Kurt Bossler	M + T(d,e) 1967 Hänssler-Verlag, Neuhausen-Stuttgart	M + T(d) (HE 19.409) Bausteine für den Gottesdienst (e) Cantate Domino III.
128	T: (O: d) Johannes Zwick (e) Fred Kaan. M: Johann Walter	T: (e) Fred Kaan	T: (e) Cantate Domino III
129	T: (O: e) Charles Wesley. M: Orlando Gibbons		
130	T: (O: taiwanese) John E. Y. Cheng (mandarin) I-tò Lòh (e) Erik Routley. M: I-tò Lòh	M + T(mandarin) I-to Loh (e) Erik Routley	
131	T: (O: un) Kiràly Imre von Pécselyi (e) Erik Routley. M: Hungarian melody. Harm. Cantate Domino	T: (e) 1976 Hinshaw Music Inc.	T: (e) *Westminster Praise*
132	T: (tr: e) Nicol Macnicol. M: Y. L. Yang. Harm. Cantate Domino	T: (e) Winslow, Godalming	M + T(e) *EACC Hymnal*
133	T: (O: e) Masao Takenaka/Fred Kaan. M: Nj. R. Sutisno. Harm. Cantate Domino	T: (e) Fred Kaan	M + T(e) *New Songs of Asian Cities*
134	T: (O: e) J. W. Chadwick. M: Orlando Gibbons		
135	T: (O: schw) Olov Hartman (e) Caryl & Ruth Micklem. M: Sven-Erik Bäck	T: (schw) Olov Hartman (e) Caryl Mickelm. M: AB Nordiska Musikförlaget/ Edition Wilhelm Hansen, Stockholm, Sweden	M + T(schw) *71 psalmer och visor*, Verbum, Stockholm (e) Cantate Domino III

Hymn No.	Writer, Translator/Composer, Arranger	Copyright Holder or Controller	Source
136	T: (O: e) Christopher Coelho refrain, verses John 17. M: Christopher Coelho	M + T(e) 1974 Agape, Carol Stream, Illinois 60187, USA. International copyright secured. Used by permission	
137	T: (O: e) Fred Kaan. M: Doreen Potter	M + T(e) 1974 Agape, Carol Stream, Illinois 60187, USA. International copyright secured. Used by permission	M + T(e) Cantate Domino III
138	T: (O: f) Lucien Deiss (e) Erik Routley. M: Lucien Deiss	M + T(f) I 46 Levain (SEFIM, Paris). (e) Erik Routley	T(e) Cantate Domino III
139(a)	T: (O: e) Brian Wren. M: Peter Cutts	M + T(e) Oxford University Press, London	M + T(e) *Dunblane Praises*
(b)	T: (O: e) Brian Wren. M: Doreen Potter. Harm. E. Routley	T(e) Oxford University Press. M: Doreen Potter	T(e) *Dunblane Praises* M: Cantate Domino III
140(a)	T: (O: e) John Oxenham. M: American folk-hymn. Arr. H. T. Burleigh	T(e) Theo Oxenham	
(b)	T: (O: e) John Oxenham. M: A. R. Reinagle	T(e) Theo Oxenham	
141	T: (O: e) Fred Kaan. M: Doreen Potter	M + T(e) 1976 Stainer & Bell Ltd., London	M + T(e) *Pilgrim Praise*
142	T: (O: d) Otmar Schulz (e) Ivor Jones. M: and Arr. Rolf Schweizer 1967	M + T(e) Hänssler-Verlag, Neuhausen-Stuttgart (d) Burckhardthaus-Verlag, Gelnhausen	M: "Liederheft 72" Beigleitsätze für Tasten-instrumente (HE 19.511)
143	T: (O: e) G. K. A. Bell. M: Melchior Vulpius 1609. Harm. F. Layriz	T: (e) Oxford University Press, London	T: (e) *Songs of Praise*
144	T: (O: su) Zakarias D. Mzengi (e) Howard S. Olson. M: Ihandzu-Ilyamba melody	M + T(su,e) Lutheran Theological College, Makumira, Tanzania	
145	T: (O: f) Dominique Ombrie (e) Fred Kaan. M: Dominique Ombrie	M + T(f) D 87 Chalet (SEFIM, Paris) (e) Fred Kaan	T: (e) Cantate Domino III
146(a)	T: (O: d) Martin Luther (e) Thomas Carlyle. M: Martin Luther. Harm. Cantate Domino		
(b)	T: (O: d) Martin Luther (e) Thomas Carlyle. M: Martin Luther 1529. Harm. J. S. Bach 1739		
147	T: (O: e) Hywel Elvet Lewis. M: Thomas John Williams 1890		
148(a)	T: (O: d) Christian/Barth/ Nehring arr. Otto Riethmüller (e) F. Pratt Green. M: Geistliche Böhmische Brüder 1566	T: (e) Oxford University Press, London	M + T(d) *Schalom* (e) Cantate Domino

Hymn No.	Writer, Translator/Composer, Arranger	Copyright Holder or Controller	Source
(b)	T: (O: d) Christian/Barth/ Nehring (e) F. Pratt Green. M: Geistliche Böhmische Brüder/ Neufassung Otto Riethmüller	T: (e) Oxford University Press, London M: für Neufassung Burckhardthaus-Verlag, Gelnhausen	M + T(d) *Schalom* (e) Cantate Domino
149	T: (O: e) A. C. Ainger. M: Martin Shaw	T: (e) non-copyright. M: Oxford University Press, London	M + T(e) *Songs of Praise*
150	T: (O: d) John 20. M: Paul Ernst Ruppel 1965	M: Hänssler-Verlag, Neuhausen-Stuttgart	M + T(d) *Bausteine für den Gottesdienst* (HE 19.301)
151	T: (O: d) J. A. Cramer (e) Fred Kaan. M: and Arr. J. Crüger Harm. Cantate Domino	T: (e) Fred Kaan	T(e) Cantate Domino III *Bausteine für den Gottesdienst* (HE 301)
152	T: (O: greek) Liturgy of St James (e) G. Moultrie. M: French carol melody. Harm. Ralph Vaughan Williams 1906		
153	T: (O: e) Negro Spiritual. M: Negro Spiritual. Harm. Charles Cleall 1969		
154	T: (O: e) G. W. Briggs. M: Alfred M. Smith	T: (e) Oxford University Press, London. M: Mrs A. M. Smith	M + T(e) *Songs of Praise*
155	T: (O: e) Percy Dearmer. M: Lee Hastings Bristol Jr.	M: Lee Hastings Bristol (e) Oxford University Press, London	T: (e) *Songs of Praise*
156	T: (O: e) Dermott Monahan. M: Urdu melody. Harm. F. B. Westbrook	M: harm. Oxford University Press, London	M + T(e) *EACC Hymnal*
157(a)	T: (O: chinese) Timothy Tingfang Lew (e) W. R. O. Taylor. M: Su Yin-Lan 1934. Harm. *BBC Hymnbook* 1951	M + T(chinese,e) Christian Conference of Asia, Singapore	M + T(chinese,e) *EACC Hymnal*
(b)	Pentatonic. Harm. Cantate Domino		
158	T: (O: e) Fred Kaan. M: Stanley L. Osborne	T: (e) 1976 Stainer & Bell Ltd., London. M: Stanley L. Osborne	The *Hymnbook* of the United and Anglican Church of Canada
159	T: (O: d) Dieter Trautwein (e) F. Pratt Green. M: Dieter Trautwein	M + T(d) Burckhardthaus-Verlag, Gelnhausen-Stuttgart (e) Oxford University Press, London	M + T(d) *Schalom* (e) Cantate Domino III
160	T: (O: e) Fred Kaan. M: *Grenoble Antiphoner* 1746	T: (e) 1976 Stainer & Bell Ltd., London	

Hymn No.	Writer, Translator/Composer, Arranger	Copyright Holder or Controller	Source
161	T: (O: e) F. Bland Tucker. M: La Forme des Prières, Strasbourg		M + T(e) *Hymnal* 1940
162	T: (O: schw) Olov Hartman (e) Fred Kaan. M: Sven-Erik Bäck	T: (schw) Olov Hartman (e) 1976 Stainer & Bell Ltd., London. M: AB Nordiska Musikförlaget/Edition Wilhelm Hansen, Stockholm, Sweden	M + T(schw) *Psalmer och visor* 76, Verbum, Stockholm (e) Cantate Domino III
163(a)	T: (O: d) Philipp Nicolai (e) F. C. Burkitt. M: Philipp Nicolai	T: (e) Oxford University Press, London	M + T(d) Cantate Domino II. T: (e) *English Hymnal* (original title: Wake, O wake with tidings thrilling)
(b)	M: Philipp Nicolai. Harm. J. S. Bach		
164	T: (O: e) C. W. Humphreys. M: Gustav Holst	T: (e) non-copyright. M: Oxford University Press, London	M + T(e) *English Hymnal*
165	T: (O: f) Claude Rozier (e) Emily Chisholm. M: Claude Rozier	M + T(f) W 14 Seuil (SEFIM, Paris) (e) Emily Chisholm	
166	T: (O: greek) M: Byzantine 15th century. tr: and Arr. by D. E. Conomos	M + translation: D. E. Conomos	
167(a)	T: (O: russian) M: Kievan melody		
(b)	T: (e) anonymous translation of 167a for Kievan melody		
168	T: (O: serbian) (e) anonymous. M: Traditional Serbian melody		
169	T: (O: serbian) (e) anonymous. M: Traditional Serbian melody		
170	T: (O: rumanian) M: Traditional Rumanian melody		
171	T: (O: greek) M: Byzantine 15th century. tr: and Arr. by D. E. Conomos	M + translation: D. E. Conomos	
172	T: (O: greek) M: Byzantine 15th century. tr: and Arr. D. E. Conomos	Music and translation: D. E. Conomos	
173	T: (O: greek) M: Byzantine 15th century. tr: and Arr. D. E. Conomos	Music and translation: D. E. Conomos	
174	T: (O: russian) (e) anonymous. M: Russian Orthodox chant		Cantate Domino II
175	T: (O: bulgarian) (e) anonymous. M: Traditional Bulgarian chant		

Hymn No.	Writer, Translator/Composer, Arranger	Copyright Holder or Controller	Source
176	T: (O: russian) (e) M. M. Gowen. M: Russian Orthodox liturgy		Cantate Domino II
177	T: (O: rumanian) M: Traditional Rumanian		
178	T: (O: coptic) M: Coptic Orthodox		
179	T: (O: coptic) M: Coptic Orthodox		
180	T: (O: greek) M: Ancient Gallican melody		
181	T: (O: f) (e) Erik Routley. M: J. Berthier	T+M: F 156 A.E.L.F./ Fleurus (SEFIM, Paris) (e) Erik Routley	
182	T: (O: latin) (e) David S. Goodall. M: J. Gelineau and M. Chappuis. Arr. David Goodall	M(arr.)+T(e) David S. Goodall	
183	T: (O: f) M: Association Episcopale Liturgique pour les Pays Francophones (A.E.L.F.) Harm. Cantate Domino		
184	T: (O: f) Joseph Gelineau. M: Joseph Gelineau	T: (f) Cantate Domino (WCC). M: SEFIM, Paris	
185	T: (O: latin) M: Vatican XVII		
186	T: (O: e) John Erickson. M:	M+T(e) John Erickson	
187	T: (O: e) John Erickson. M: John Erickson	M+T(e) John Erickson	
188	M: Herbert Beuerle	M: Fidula-Verlag, Boppard und Salzburg	*Gnadenquell*
189	T: (O: latin) (d) Adam Gumpelzhaimer (f) J. Gelineau M: Adam Gumpelzhaimer		
190	T: (O: d) Albert Thate. M: Albert Thate	M+T(d) Bärenreiter-Verlag, Kassel, Tours, London	*Geistliche Zwiegesänge*
191	M+T 1529. 1964 Kanon von Richard Rudolf Klein	M: (Kanon) Fidual-Verlag, Boppard and Salzburg	
192	T: (O: f) M: Abraham Tétouom, Caméroun		
193	T: (O: hindi) M: from India		
194	T: (O: d) George Weissel (e) Catherine Winkworth. M: Paul Ernst Ruppel based on "Macht hoch die Tür" (Freylinghausen 1715)	M+Kanon: Verlag Singende Gemeinde, Wuppertal	*Evangelisches Kirchengesang Buch*
195	T: Lee Hastings Bristol Jr. M: Lee Hastings Bristol Jr.	M+T(e) Abingdon Press 1970, Nashville, Tennessee, USA	M+T(e) *Let the Children Sing*

Hymn No.	Writer, Translator/Composer, Arranger	Copyright Holder or Controller	Source
196	T: (O: d) Hermann Stern. M: Hermann Stern	M + T(d) Verlag Merseburger, Berlin	
197	T: (O: d) Paul Gerhardt. M: Herbert Beuerle from a melody by J. Crüger	M: Burckhardthaus-Verlag, Neuhausen–Stuttgart	*Mein Dudelsack*
198	T: (O: d) Hermann Stern. M: Hermann Stern	M + T(d) Verlag Merseburger, Berlin	
199	T: (O: d) Gerd Watkinson. M: Gerd Watkinson	M + T(d) Voggenreiter-Verlag, Bonn–Bad Godesberg	
200	T: (O: hindi) M: An Indian Blessing, Gazar		
201	T: (O: d) Helmut König. M: An Israeli Blessing (e) Erik Routley	M + T(d) Voggenreiter-Verlag, Bonn–Bad Godesberg.	
202	M: Paul Ernst Ruppel	M: Verlag Merseburger, Berlin	*Das Monatslied*, Heft 1

Psalms · Psalmen · Psaumes

1 Psalm 99 (100)

Switzerland
Psalm 134 in Octante-trois Pseaumes
Geneva 1551. Harm. C. Goudimel 1562

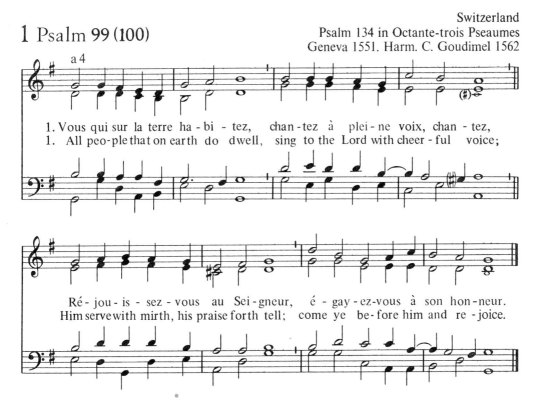

1. Vous qui sur la terre ha - bi - tez, chan-tez à plei - ne voix, chan - tez,
1. All peo-ple that on earth do dwell, sing to the Lord with cheer - ful voice;

Ré - jou - is - sez - vous au Sei - gneur, é - gay - ez-vous à son hon-neur.
Him serve with mirth, his praise forth tell; come ye be - fore him and re - joice.

2. Lui seul est notre souverain, / c'est lui qui nous fit de sa main: / nous le peuple qu'il mènera, / le troupeau qu'il rassemblera.

3. Dans sa maison dès aujourd'hui, / tous présentez-vous devant lui; / célébrez son nom glorieux, / exaltez-le jusques aux cieux.

4. Pour toi, Seigneur, que notre amour / se renouvelle chaque jour: / ta bonté, ta fidélité, / demeurent pour l'éternité.

R. Chapal 1970

2. The Lord ye know is God indeed; / without our aid he did us make; / we are his folk, he doth us feed, / and for his sheep he doth us take.

3. O enter then his gates with praise; / approach with joy his courts unto; / praise, laud, and bless his name always, / for it is seemly so to do.

4. For why, the Lord our God is good; / his mercy is for ever sure; / his truth at all times firmly stood, / and shall from age to age endure.

William Kethe 1560

1

2 Psalm 89 (90)

St. Anne

England
Melody and bass attr. to William Croft 1708
Rhythm modernised

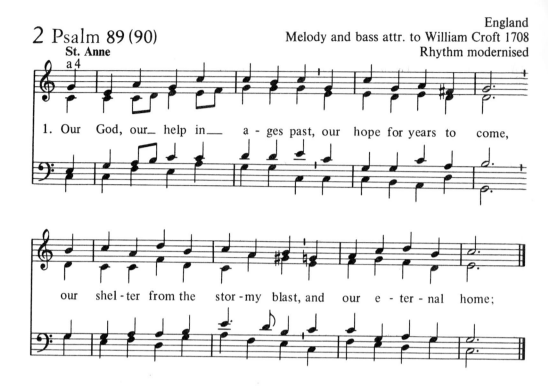

1. Our God, our help in ages past, our hope for years to come, our shelter from the stormy blast, and our eternal home;

2. Under the shadow of thy throne / thy saints have dwelt secure; / sufficient is thine arm alone, / and our defence is sure.

3. Before the hills in order stood, / or earth received her frame, / from everlasting thou art God, / to endless years the same.

4. A thousand ages in thy sight / are like an evening gone, / short as the watch that ends the night / before the rising sun.

5. Our God, our help in ages past, / our hope for years to come, / be thou our guard while troubles last, / and our eternal home.

Isaac Watts 1719 (from Ps. 90)

3 Psalm 135 (136)

China
Buddhist Temple chant

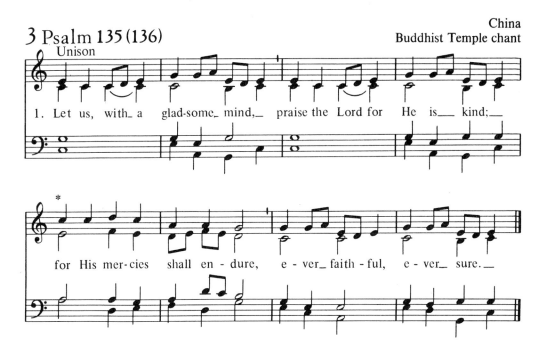

Unison

1. Let us, with a glad-some mind, praise the Lord for He is kind;
for His mer-cies shall en-dure, e - ver faith - ful, e - ver sure.

*popular version, not in Melody Edition, but may be used.

2. He with all-commanding might, / filled the new-made world with light; / For His mercies . . .

3. He His chosen race did bless / in the wasteful wilderness; /

4. He hath, with a piteous eye, / looked upon our misery; /

5. Let us then with gladsome mind / praise the Lord for He is kind: /

after John Milton (1608–1674)

4 Psalms 41/42 (42/43)

Switzerland
Octante-trois Pseaumes
Geneva 1551. Harm. C.D.

1. Comme un cerf al - té - ré bra - me pour-chas-sant le frais_ des eaux,
1. Seek - ing wa - ter, seek-ing shel - ter gasps the thirs - ty, wea - ry deer.

O Sei-gneur, ain - si mon â - me sou - pire a - près tes_ ruis - seaux.
So my soul, in days of trou - ble, longs for God's re - fresh-ment_ here.

Elle a soif du Dieu vi - vant et s'é - crie en le cher-chant:
In this stress-ful course of life, in its lone - li - ness and strife,

O mon Dieu, quand donc se - ra - ce que mes yeux ver-ront ta_ fa - ce?
'When', say I, 'will God de - li - ver? Is his mer - cy gone for_ e - ver?'

In Melody Edition, one tone higher

4

2. Tu es seul ma forteresse; / comment peux-tu m'oublier, / quand tu vois ceux qui me pressent, / ne cessant de me railler? / Montre-toi mon défenseur / contre tous mes oppresseurs; / me faut-il marcher sans trêve / dans un deuil que rien n'achève?

3. Dans ma nuit mets ta lumière, / dans mon cœur ta verité, / pour guider jusqu'à son père / le retour de l'exilé. / A nouveau Dieu de ma joie, / je ferai monter vers toi / avec tous ceux qui te chantent, / ma ferveur reconnaissante.

4. Mais pourquoi mon âme encore / frémis-tu d'un tel effroi, / quand déjà paraît l'aurore / et que Dieu est près de toi? / Tourne-toi vers ton Sauveur, / il apaisera ton cœur; / et tes chants loueront encore / le Seigneur que tu adores.

R. Chapal 1970

2. No! he is my soul's true fortress; / though I hear those voices wild, / 'Where's your God, perchance he sleepeth!' / he will not forget his child. / Come, then, be my advocate; / come, your servant vindicate: / then no more in fruitless sorrow / will I face a barren morrow.

3. Send your light and truth to lead me, / then the path shall I discern / to my father's house, where welcome / greets the prodigal's return. / Then new songs shall fill my days, / every moment full of praise / with the faithful who surround him, / with the blest ones who have found him!

4. So, my soul, why such disquiet? / Why such mourning, why such fear? / Day already breaks on darkness; / God has sought you. God is near. / Hope in God, and you shall live; / all delight he waits to give, / peace and power and every blessing / you shall know, this faith possessing.

Erik Routley 1972

5 Psalm 137 (138)

France
Pseaulmes cinquante de David
Lyon, 1547 Harm. C. Goudimel 1562

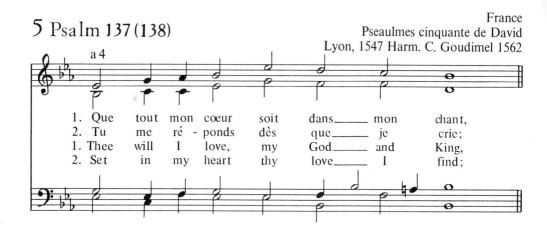

a 4

1. Que tout mon cœur soit dans mon chant,
2. Tu me ré - ponds dès que je crie;
1. Thee will I love, my God and King,
2. Set in my heart thy love I find;

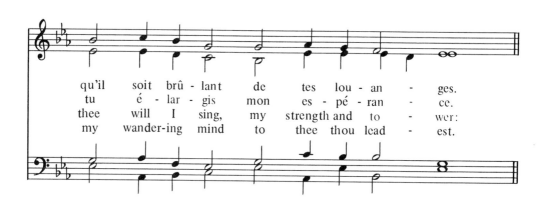

qu'il soit brû - lant de tes lou - an - ges.
tu é - lar - gis mon es - pé - ran - ce.
thee will I sing, my strength and to - wer:
my wander-ing mind to thee thou lead - est.

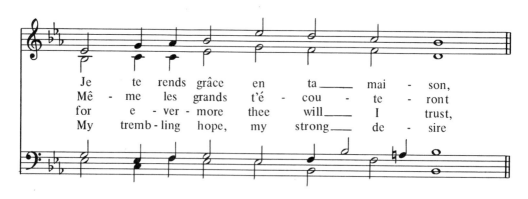

Je te rends grâce en ta mai - son,
Mê - me les grands t'é - cou - te - ront
for e - ver - more thee will I trust,
My tremb - ling hope, my strong de - sire

6

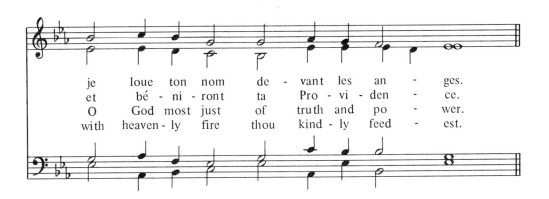

je loue ton nom de - vant les an - ges.
et bé - ni - ront ta Pro - vi - den - ce.
O God most just of truth and po - wer.
with heaven - ly fire thou kind - ly feed - est.

Tu es ve - nu pour e - xal - ter
Ton saint a - mour, ô roi des cieux,
Thou all things hast in or - der placed,
Lo, all things fair thy path pre - pare,

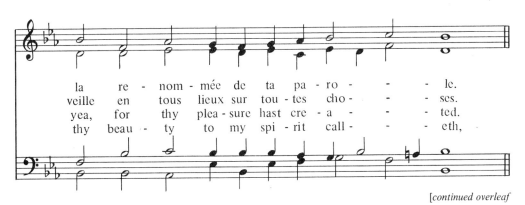

la re - nom - mée de ta pa - ro - le.
veille en tous lieux sur tou - tes cho - ses.
yea, for thy plea - sure hast cre - a - ted.
thy beau - ty to my spi - rit call - eth,

[continued overleaf

J'a - do - re ta fi - dé - li - té
Dans ses pro - jets tu suis des yeux
And on thy throne, un - seen, un - known,
thine to re - main in joy or pain,

et ta bon - té qui me con - so - lent.
l'homme or - gueil - leux, tu en dis - po - ses.
reign - est a - lone in glo - ry seat - ed.
and count it gain what - e'er be - fall - eth.

3. Ta paix, mon Dieu, dure à toujours; / c'est ton amour qui me délivre / quand je suis le plus éprouvé / ton bras levé me fait revivre. / Et quand je suis au désespoir / c'est ton pouvoir qui me relève. / Ce qu'il t'a plu de commencer / sans se lasser ta main l'achève.

R. Chapal 1970

3. O more and more thy love extend, / my life befriend with heavenly pleasure; / that I may win thy paradise, / thy pearl of price, thy countless treasure; / since but in thee I can go free / from earthly care and vain oppression, / this prayer I make for Jesu's sake / that thou me take in thy possession.

Robert Bridges 1899

6 Psalm 97 (98)

Switzerland
Octante-trois Pseaumes
Geneva 1551 Harm. John Wilson 1964

1. En - ton - nons un nou - veau can - ti - que
1. New songs of ce - le - bra - tion ren - der

pour cé - lé - brer le Dieu___ sau - veur;
to him who has great won - ders done;

ce qu'il a fait est ma - gni - fi - que
awed by his power his foes sur - ren - der

le - vant pour nous un bras vain - queur.
and___ fall be - fore the might - y One.

[continued overleaf

9

Le sa - lut de Dieu se___ ré - vè - le
He has made known his great___ sal - va - tion

et tous les yeux l'ont re - con - nu;
which all his friends with joy con - fess;

de proche en pro - che la nou - vel - le
he has re - vealed to eve - ry na - tion

jusqu' au bout du monde___ a cou - ru.
his e - ver - last - ing___ right - eous - ness.

2. Chantez pour lui vos chants de fête; / psalmodiez! criez de joie! / Au son du cor et des trompettes, / acclamez tous le Roi des rois. / Le Seigneur vient juger la terre, / sa vérité va s'imposer. / Que tous les peuples qui espèrent / en l'apprenant soient apaisés.

3. Que tous les océans mugissent; / fleuves aussi, battez des mains: / et que les montagnes bondissent / pour acclamer le Roi qui vient. / Le Seigneur va juger le monde / avec droiture et vérité, / et partout sa justice fonde / son éternelle royauté.

R. Chapal 1970

2. Joyfully, heartily resounding, / let every instrument and voice / peal out the praise of grace abounding, / calling the whole world to rejoice. / Trumpets and organs set in motion / such sounds as make the heavens ring: / all things that live in earth and ocean / make music for your mighty King.

3. Rivers and seas and torrents roaring, / honour the Lord with wild acclaim; / mountains and stones look up adoring / and find a voice to praise his name. / Righteous, commanding, ever glorious, / praises be his that never cease: / just is our God, whose truth victorious / establishes the world in peace.

Erik Routley 1972

7 Psalm 1

Thailand
Traditional melody
Arr. Erik Routley, 1975

Unison   **Sri Lampang**

1. ความ สุข ยืน ยง คง มา สู่ ทำ ผู้ ชอบ ผู้ กอปร ด้วย
2. ได้ ความ จำ เริญ เพลิด เพลิน จิต ชน รื่น บาน เหมือนพฤกษ์ ตระ

1. Hap-py is he who walks in God's wise way, hap-py who
2. His is the life where du-ty and de-light nou-rish each

ใจ มั่น ใน ศรัท ธา พา ใจ เดิน ตาม บัญ ญัติ พระ
การ ริม ธาร เบี่ยม ชล ก้าน กิ่ง สด เขียว ไม่ เหี่ยว แห้ง

shuns the sin-ful choice: hap-py who finds his plea-sure
o-ther bliss-ful-ly; as when be-side a broad and

ยะ โฮ วา เดิน ใน มรร คา ปวง สา ธุ ชน
เมื่อ แล้ง ฝน ไม้ ดอก ออก ผล ตาม กาล เว ลา

in God's law, hap-py who heeds God's right-eous voice.
gen'-rous stream proud-ly stands e-ver-green the tree.

12

3. ผ่าย ทาง คน ชั่ว หา เป็น ดั่ง เช่น นั้น ไม่ เหมือน แกลบ กระจาย ตาม สาย
ลม พา ดัง นั้น คน ชั่ว จะ ต้อง ทน เวทนา วัน เมื่อ ราชา พิพากษา คน

4. กิจการ คน ชั่ว ย่อม วิบัติ ย่อย ยับ ไป ทำ ไว้ อย่าง ไร ย่อม ได้ แก่ ตน
แต่ ความ ชอบ ธรรม ย่อม นำ คน ให้ ได้ ดล บรรล ยัง ผล ดัง ตน มุ่ง ปอง

3. Fretful and anxious are the sinner's days, / barren and lonely is his path; / like wind on dust the judgment of the Lord / scatters his pride in sudden wrath.

4. Lord, in your mercy spare me, keep me still, / let me not choose the sinner's way: / promise and law you equally have given: / let them be my delight today.

Erik Routley 1972

8 Psalm 8

Unison

1. Lord, how ma - jes - tic is your name; the earth and sky a - dore you, the mouth of ba - bies sings your praise and child - ren dance_____ be - fore you.

2. When I look up and see the stars / and think of space unending, / I marvel that you care for man, / and with your love befriend him.

3. You lift him to the very height / of your creative likeness, / just as you raised your Son from death / to Easter's wideawakeness.

Fred Kaan 1968

9 Psalm 33(34)

Finland
Traditional Melody
Harm. C.D.

1. Her-ras-ta vei-saa__ kie-le-ni, y-lis-tää ar-mo-an -
1. O sing, my soul, your__ Ma-ker's praise in grate-ful hymns as-cend -

- sa Ei un-hot-taa voi__ sie-lu-ni hy-vi-ä te-ko-
- ing, whose stead-fast love has__crowned thy days with heav'n-ly gifts un -

- jan - sa. Mä et-sin ja__ hän vas - ta - si. Ja nöy-rät
- end - ing. I sought the Lord,__ he heard__ my cry; his ho-ly

kuu-li rie-mu-ni ja loh-du-tuk-sen sai - vat.
an-gels ho-ver__ nigh the tents of__ those__ who love__ him.

[vv. 2, 3 overleaf

15

2. Ne, jotka häntä etsivät / saa avun hältä armaan. / Ne, jotka häntä pelkäävät, / hän varjeleepi varmaan. / Ja ahdingonkin aikana / he tuntea saa iloa, / kun Herra heitä hoitaa.

3. Kasvoihin Herran katsokaa, / ne loistaa suloisesti. / Ja hyvyyttänsä maistakaa, / mi vuotaa iäisesti. / On autuas se ihminen, / ken turvas yksin hänehen, / ei mitään hältä puutu.

Julius Krohn 1835-1888

2. The Lord is good to those who seek / his face in time of sorrow; / he giveth strength unto the weak, / and grace for each tomorrow. / Though grief may tarry for the night, / the morn shall break in joy and light / with blessings from his presence.

3. The Lord will turn his face in peace / when troubled souls draw near him; / his loving kindness ne'er shall cease / to them that trust and fear him. / Our God will not forsake his own, / eternal is his heav'nly throne; / his kingdom stands for ever.

E. E. Ryden and Toivo Harjunpää 1962

10 Psalm 35 (36)

Germany
Rolf Schweizer 1964

1. Herr, dei-ne Gü — te reicht so weit der Him-mel ist,
1. Your lov-ing kind — ness is as wide as noon-day sky,

und dei - ne Wahr-heit so weit die Wol-ken ge –hen. Dei - ne Ge - rech-
your faith-ful love goes as high as clouds in sum-mer. Your righ-teous judg-

-tig - keit steht wie die Ber – ge, und dein Ge - richt ist tief —
-ments stand strong as the moun - tains and your pro-nounce-ments deep

wie das Meer. Men-schen und Tie - ren willst du ein Ge-hil - fe sein.
as the sea. Men and the crea - tures live in your pro-tec-ting love.

17

[vv. 2, 3, 4 overleaf

2. Laßt mich begreifen, Herr, was deine Güte ist, / und deine Wahrheit, von der ich nichts verstehe. / Täglich umgeben mich Worte und Stimmen; / aber ich höre gar nicht mehr hin, / weil sie vom vielen Reden ganz verdorben sind.

3. Gib du doch Sinn, Herr, allem, was ich sag und tu, / Heilgen Geist gib in hilflose Gedanken, / daß ich dich rufen kann, wenn ich nichts höre, / daß ich dich höre, wenn du mich rufst, / daß ich gehorche, wenn du mich berufen willst.

4. Herr, deine Güte reicht so weit der Himmel ist, / und deine Wahrheit, so weit die Wolken gehen. / Dein Flügelschatten ist unsre Bewahrung, / aus deinem Leben, leben wir auch; / und wir erkennen erst in deinem Licht das Licht.

Gerhard Valentin 1964

2. Give me to know, Lord, what your lovingkindness is, / your faithful guidance of which I know but nothing. / Voices and words, O Lord, surround me daily, / but I no longer hear what they say. / They are confused by talking and the strife of tongues.

3. O Lord, give meaning in all that I say and do, / your Holy Spirit in all my helpless thinking, / that I may call on you when I hear nothing, / that I may hear your voice when you call, / and be obedient when you call me to your work.

4. Your lovingkindness is as wide as noonday sky, / your faithful love goes as high as clouds in summer. / Your wings outspread above are our protection, / your life, our Father God, is our life; / and it is only in your light we see the light.

Emily Chisholm 1972

11 Psalm 102 (103)

Malagasy
Traditional melody 1818
Harm. C.D.

Unison

1. Mi - sao - ra an' i___ Za - na - ha - ry. 'Zao o -
1. Bless the Lord, my soul, and all that is with-in me, bless his

- lo - na___ to - nto - l'i - zao. Di - a___
name and call on___ him, and re-mem-ber his word. He will for -

man - ka___ la - za___ A - - - zy
- give all your in - i - qui-ty and heal all___ your dis - ease.

F'an - to n'i - zao___ re - he - tr'i - zao.
Bless the Lord, my soul, and all that is with - in me.

[vv. 2, 3 overleaf

19

2. Izay zavatra nomeny / mahafaly mahasoa / toy ny andro fararano / to'ny andro mipoaka.

3. Di' ampitomboy ny sainay / hahalala ny teninao. / Hahafantatra marina / Izay sitraky ny fonao.

2. For the Lord is merciful and ever gracious, / slow to anger on his folk, but abounding in love. / He will not always chide nor will he keep his anger evermore. / For the Lord is merciful and ever gracious.

3. As a Father, so the Lord pities his children, / those who keep his holy word, and remember his will. / He has established his kingdom over heav'n and over earth. / As a Father, so the Lord pities his children.

U.S. Leupold 1969

12 Psalm 112 (113)

Jamaica
Barry Chevannes 1971
Harm. C.D.

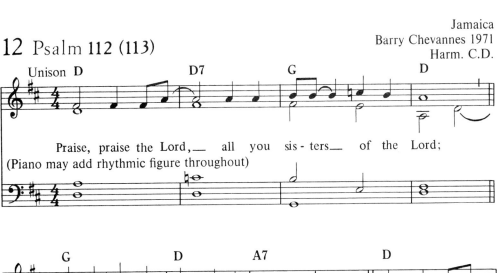

Praise, praise the Lord,— all you sis - ters— of the Lord;
(Piano may add rhythmic figure throughout)

may his name be blest for— ev - er - more. Praise, praise the Lord,—

— all you bro - thers of the Lord; praise his name from

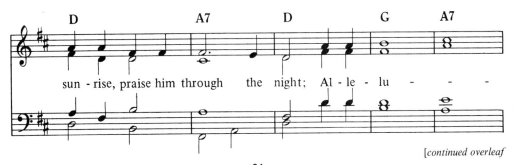

sun - rise, praise him through the night; Al - le - lu - - -

[continued overleaf

21

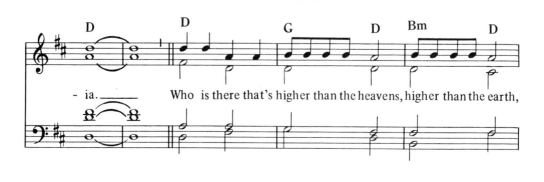

- ia.＿ Who is there that's higher than the heavens, higher than the earth,

God a - lone, and there ＿ is none like him!＿

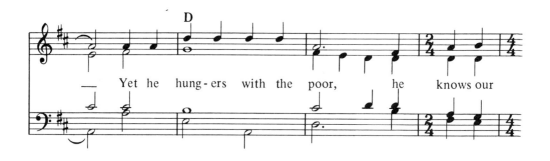

＿ Yet he hung-ers with the poor, he knows our

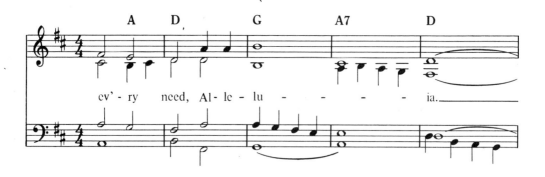

ev'-ry need, Al- le - lu - - - - ia.＿

23

13a Psalm 112 (113)

Germany
Heinz Werner Zimmermann 1970

Unison

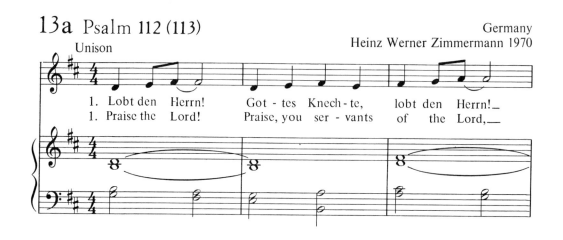

1. Lobt den Herrn! Got - tes Knech - te, lobt den Herrn!_
1. Praise the Lord! Praise, you ser - vants of the Lord,—

Lobt den Na - men des Herrn!_ Hei - lig__ ist der Na - me des Herrn,
praise the name of the Lord!_ Bless-ed__ be the name of the Lord!

hei – lig,__ hei – lig, na - he und fern,_ von An - be - ginn und in
Bles - sed__ be the name of the Lord_ from this time forth and for

24

E - wig - keit! Lobt den Herrn!_ Lobt den Herrn!_
ev - er - more! Praise the Lord, _ Praise the Lord!_

2. Lobt den Herrn! / Tag für Tag lobt Gott, den Herrn, / der den Atem
uns gab. / An die rechte Stelle uns stellt, / uns in seiner Gnade erhält, /
uns helfen kommt und uns helfen hilft. / Lobt den Herrn! / Lobt den
Herrn!

3. Lobt den Herrn! / Auch die Nacht lobt Gott, den Herrn, / und das
ferne Gestirn. / Wo auch immer Unheil geschah: / auch im Dunkel bleibt
er uns nah, / spricht Mut uns zu, macht uns unverzagt. / Lobt den
Herrn! / Lobt den Herrn!

4. Lobt den Herrn! / Gottes Knechte, lobt den Herrn! / Lobt den Namen
des Herrn! / Heimatlose bringt er nach Haus, / führt sie aus dem Elend
heraus, / erfüllt ihr Leben mit neuem Sinn. / Lobt den Herrn! / Lobt den
Herrn!

Heinz Werner Zimmermann 1972

2. Praise the Lord! / Thanks and praises sing to God, / day by day to the
Lord! / High above the nations is God, / high above the nations is God, /
his glory high over earth and sky. / Praise the Lord! / Praise the Lord!

3. Praise the Lord! / Praise and glory give to God! / Who is like unto
him? / Raising up the poor from the dust, / raising up the poor from the
dust, / he makes them dwell in his heart and home. / Praise the Lord! /
Praise the Lord!

4. Praise the Lord! / Praise, you servants of the Lord! / Praise the love
of the Lord! / Giving to the homeless a home, / giving to the homeless a
home, / he fills their hearts with new hope and joy. / Praise the Lord! /
Praise the Lord!

Marjorie Jillson 1970

13b Psalm 112 (113)

Germany
Heinz Werner Zimmermann 1970

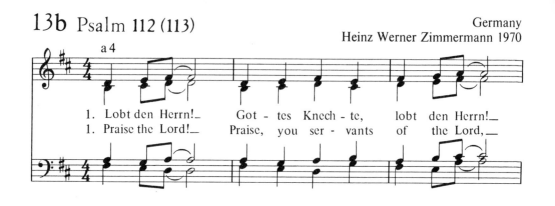

1. Lobt den Herrn!_ Got - tes Knech - te, lobt den Herrn!_
1. Praise the Lord!_ Praise, you ser - vants of the Lord, _

Lobt den Na - men des Herrn!_ Hei - lig_ ist der Na - me des Herrn,
praise the name of the Lord!_ Bless - ed_ be the name of the Lord!

Hei - lig ist der Na - me des Herrn,
Bles - sed be the name of the Lord!

hei - lig, _ hei - lig, na - he und fern, _ von An - be - ginn und in
Bless - ed_ be the name of the Lord_ from this time forth and for

hei - lig, hei - lig, na - he und fern, von An - be - ginn und in
Bles - sed be the name of the Lord from this time forth and for

26

E - wig - keit! Lobt den Herrn!_ Lobt den Herrn!_
ev - er - more! Praise the Lord, _ Praise the Lord!_

E - wig - keit! Lobt_ den Herrn! Lobt_ den Herrn!
ev - er - more! Praise _ the Lord,_ Praise_ the Lord!_

2. Lobt den Herrn! / Tag für Tag lobt Gott, den Herrn, / der den Atem uns gab. / An die rechte Stelle uns stellt, / uns in seiner Gnade erhält, / uns helfen kommt und uns helfen hilft. / Lobt den Herrn! / Lobt den Herrn!

3. Lobt den Herrn! / Auch die Nacht lobt Gott, den Herrn, / und das ferne Gestirn. / Wo auch immer Unheil geschah: / auch im Dunkel bleibt er uns nah, / spricht Mut uns zu, macht uns unverzagt. / Lobt den Herrn! / Lobt den Herrn!

4. Lobt den Herrn! / Gottes Knechte, lobt den Herrn! / Lobt den Namen des Herrn! / Heimatlose bringt er nach Haus, / führt sie aus dem Elend heraus, / erfüllt ihr Leben mit neuem Sinn. / Lobt den Herrn! / Lobt den Herrn!

Heinz Werner Zimmermann 1972

2. Praise the Lord! / Thanks and praises sing to God, / day by day to the Lord! / High above the nations is God, / high above the nations is God, / his glory high over earth and sky. / Praise the Lord! / Praise the Lord!

3. Praise the Lord! / Praise and glory give to God! / Who is like unto him? / Raising up the poor from the dust, / raising up the poor from the dust, / he makes them dwell in his heart and home. / Praise the Lord! / Praise the Lord!

4. Praise the Lord! / Praise, you servants of the Lord! / Praise the love of the Lord! / Giving to the homeless a home, / giving to the homeless a home, / he fills their hearts with new hope and joy. / Praise the Lord! / Praise the Lord!

Marjorie Jillson 1970

14 Psalm 136 (137)

Latvia
Traditional melody,
arr. John Ylvisaker. Harm. C.D.

1. By the Ba - by - lo - nian ri - vers we sat down in grief and wept;

hung our harps up - on a wil - low, mourn'd for Zi - on while we slept.

2. There our captors, in derision, / did require of us a song; / so we sat with staring vision / and the days were hard and long.

3. How shall we sing the Lord's song / in a strange and bitter land; / can our voices veil the sorrow? / Lord God hear your lonely band.

4. Let your cross be benediction / for men bound in tyranny; / by the power of resurrection / loose them from captivity.

Ewald Bash 1964

15 Psalm 148

England
Elizabeth Poston 1971

Praise God   Unison

1. All things that are praise God by what they are,

their be-ing speaks to us of God who is; so we may call on

them to praise his name, to give with us the ho-nour that is his.

Organ pedal

cresc.

(Last time ᵖ·*)*

2. Praise God, all angels, made by him to be / forever in the service of his throne; / shine, sun and moon, all stars whose light we see, / and by your shining make his great light known.

3. Praise God, all earthly things which he has made, / come, cold of winter, heat of summer sun; / come, spring and autumn, change and change again, / show in your changing how his will is done.

4. Praise God, all lands and seas, all living things, / all trees and plants that he has made to grow; / all birds and beasts, praise, each in your own way, / his greatness, which all things created show.

5. Praise God, all men and women, young and old: / creation's highest praise is yours to sing / to honour God, to praise with every praise / His Being, everywhere, in everything.   Brian Foley 1971

29

16 Psalm 91 (92)

Germany
Rolf Schweizer 1966

1. Das ist ein köst-lich Ding, dem Her-ren dan - ken, und lob -
1. How good to of - fer thanks to God our Fa - ther, to play in

- sin-gen dei - nem Na - men, das ist ein köst-lich Ding, dem Her-ren
ho-nour of th'Al - migh - ty! How good to of - fer thanks to God our

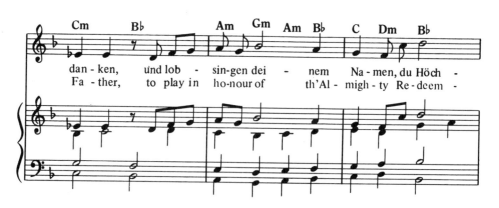

dan - ken, und lob - sin-gen dei - nem Na - men, du Höch -
Fa - ther, to play in ho-nour of th'Al - migh - ty Re-deem -

Fine

- ster.
- er!

1. Des Mor - gens dei - ne Gna - de
2. Du läßt uns fröh - lich sin - gen
1. To sing your love at day - break,
2. You make us shout in tri - umph,

und des Nachts dei - ne Wahr - heit ver - kün - di - gen auf
von den Wer - ken, die, Herr, dei - ne Hand__ ge - macht. Wie
and your mer - cy and faith - ful - ness ev' - ry night; with
and with joy ce - le - brate all your migh - ty works; your

D.C. al Fine

den zehn Sai - ten und Psal - ter, mit spie - len auf der Har - fe.
tief sind dei - ne Ge - dan - ken; du, Höch - ster, blei - best e - wig.
ten - stringed lute and with zi - ther, with mer - ry harp to praise you!
thoughts are past un - der - stand - ing, your deeds be - yond con - ceiv - ing!

E: Ivor Jones 1972

31

17 Psalm 107 (108)

Germany
Paul Ernst Ruppel 1964

Refrain

Ich will dir dan - ken, Herr, un - ter den Völ - - kern.
I want to thank___ you, God, a - mong the peo - - ples,

Ich will dir lob - sin - gen un - ter den Leu - ten. (3) - ten.
play mu - sic to___ you a - mong all the na - tions. (3) - tions.

Fine

1. Denn dei - ne Gna - de reicht, so weit der Him - mel ist,
1. For your un - fail - ing love high in the hea - ven spreads,

und dei - ne Wahr - heit, so___ weit die Wol - ken gehn.
and your great faith - ful - ness___ ran - ges to the clouds.

2. Herr Gott erhebe weit / über den Himmel dich, / und deine Ehre weit über alle Lande.

3. Ehr sei dem Vater Gott, / Ehr sei dem Sohne Gott. / Ehr sei dem Heilgen Geist, Gott in Ewigkeit.

Paul E. Ruppel 1964

2. Rise up on high, O Lord, / fill all the universe, / and let your glory encompass all the earth.

3. To Father and to Son, / to Spirit, Three in One, / glory be given, now and to eternity.

Ivor Jones 1972

18 Psalm 148

1. O praise the King of hea - ven: O praise the King of hea - ven, all ye who are his peo - ple!

O praise the King of hea - ven, Ye prin - ces! O praise the King of

hea ven, the ho - ly gra - cious King. Ye ru - lers!

All   Solo or Choir

O praise the King of hea - ven,   Al - le - lu - ia!

All

O praise the King of hea - ven,   the ho - ly gra - cious King!__

2. O tell abroad his glory: / O tell abroad his glory, / and publish it to all men. / O tell abroad his glory / Ye fathers! / O tell abroad his glory, / the holy gracious king. / Ye mothers! / O praise the king of heaven, / Alleluia! / O praise the king of heaven, / the holy gracious king.

3. O shout aloud his praises: / O shout aloud his praises / in mountain, hill and valley. / O shout aloud his praises / Young warriors! / O shout aloud his praises, / the holy gracious king. / Ye maidens! / O praise the king of heaven, / Alleluia! / O praise the king of heaven, / the holy gracious king.

E. Mawelera Tembo 1959

35

19 Psalm 8

France
Antienne: J. Samson 1953
Psalmodie: J. Gelineau 1953

Unison Antienne

O Sei-gneur no-tre Dieu, qu'il est grand ton Nom, par tout l'u-ni-vers!
How___ great is your name O___ Lord our God, through all the___ earth!

Versets

a 1 temps = o

1. Ta majes - té su - - prême est chan- tée par des
2. A voir ton ciel, ou - vrage de tes doigts, la
3. A peine le fis - tu moindre qu'un dieu, le couron -
4. Bre - bis et bœufs tous en - semble, les
5. (Rendons gloire au Père tout puis - sant, à son

lèvres d'en - fants, de tout pe - tits; tu op - - poses ton lieu
lune et les é - toiles que tu fi - xas, qu'est-ce que l'homme que tu en
- nant de gloire et de splen - deur; tu l'éta - - blis sur
bêtes même sau - - vages, oiseaux du ciel et pois - -
Fils, Jésus Christ, le Sei - gneur, à l'Es - - prit qui ha - -

fort à l'agres - seur pour ré - duire enne - mis et re - belles.
gardes mé - moire, le fils d'A - dam que tu en prennes sou - ci?
l'œuvre de tes mains, tout fut mis par toi sous ses pieds.
- sons de la mer parcou - rant les sen - tiers des eaux,
- bite en nos cœurs, dans les siècles des siècles. / A - men!)

36

Verses

a 1 tempo = o

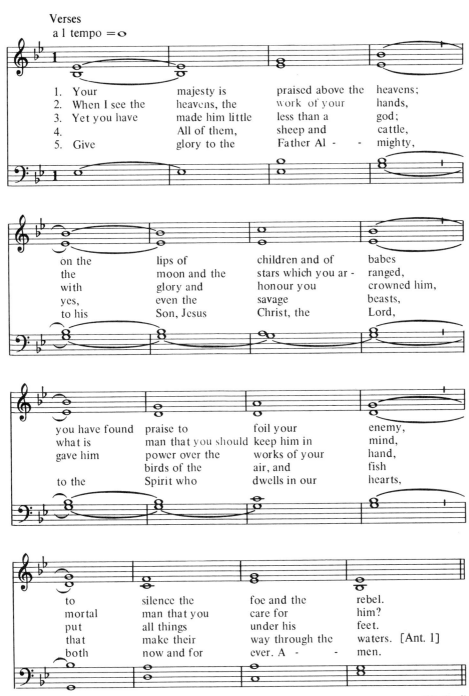

1. Your   majesty is   praised above the   heavens;
2. When I see the heavens, the   work of your   hands,
3. Yet you have   made him little   less than a   god;
4.   All of them,   sheep and   cattle,
5. Give   glory to the   Father Al -   -   mighty,

on the   lips of   children and of   babes
the   moon and the   stars which you ar - ranged,
with   glory and   honour you   crowned him,
yes,   even the   savage   beasts,
to his   Son, Jesus   Christ, the   Lord,

you have found praise to   foil your   enemy,
what is   man that you should keep him in   mind,
gave him   power over the   works of your   hand,
                birds of the   air, and   fish
to the   Spirit who   dwells in our   hearts,

to   silence the   foe and the   rebel.
mortal   man that you   care for   him?
put   all things   under his   feet.
that   make their   way through the   waters. [Ant. 1]
both   now and for   ever. A -   -   men.

(E) Grail

37

20 Psalm 22 (23)

Unison Antienne

Le Sei-gneur est mon ber - ger, rien ne sau-rait me man - quer.

A
B

1.
2. Il me
3. Devant
4.
5. Gloire au

Le Sei - gneur est mon ber - ger, je ne
guide par le juste che - - min pour l'a -
moi tu ap - prêtes une table fa -
Grâce et bon-heur m'accom - pagnent tous les
Père, au Fils, au Saint Es - prit main - te -

C

man - que de rien. Sur des prés d'herbe
- mour de son nom. Pas - se - rais-je un ra - vin de té -
- ce à mes ad - ver - saires; d'une onc - tion tu me par - fumes la
jours de ma vie; ma de - meure est la mai - son du Sei -
- nant et à ja mais; au Dieu qui est, qui é - tait et qui

*Le Psaume a cinq strophes. Les strophes 3, 4, 5 omettent les incises D et E: sauter de ⊕ à ⊕.

*The Psalm has five verses. Verses 3, 4, 5 leave out sections D and E: go straight from ⊕ to ⊕.

21 Psalm 23(24)

France
J. Gelineau 1953

Antienne
a 4

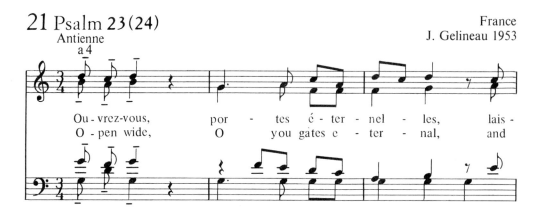

Ou - vrez-vous, por - tes é - ter - nel - les, lais -
O - pen wide, O you gates e - ter - nal, and

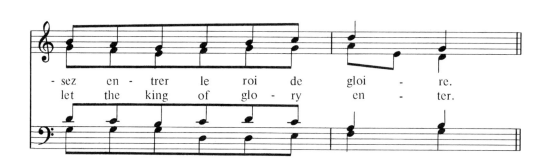

- sez en - trer le roi de gloi - re.
let the king of glo - ry en - ter.

Versets   omit in verses 4—8

1. Au Sei - gneur la   terre et sa pléni - tude,   le   monde et
2. Qui monte - ra sur la mon - tagne du Sei - gneur,   et   qui se tien-
3. A   lui la béné - diction du Sei - gneur,   la jus - tice du
4.   Portes, le - vez vos fron - tons,
5.   Qui est ce roi de   gloire?
6.   Portes, le - vez vos fron - tons,
7.   Qui est ce roi de   gloire?
8. Rendons gloire au   Père tout puis - sant,

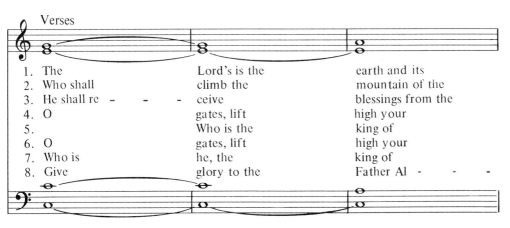

[continued overleaf

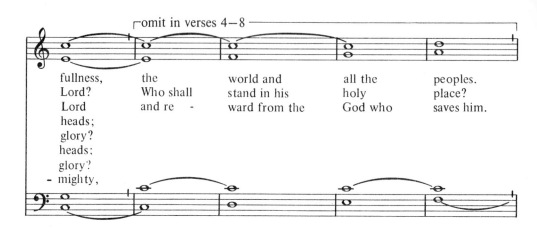

omit in verses 4—8

fullness,	the	world and	all the	peoples.
Lord?	Who shall	stand in his	holy	place?
Lord	and re -	ward from the	God who	saves him.
heads;				
glory?				
heads;				
glory?				
- mighty,				

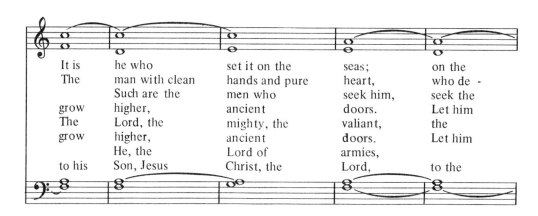

It is	he who	set it on the	seas;	on the
The	man with clean	hands and pure	heart,	who de -
	Such are the	men who	seek him,	seek the
grow	higher,	ancient	doors.	Let him
The	Lord, the	mighty, the	valiant,	the
grow	higher,	ancient	doors.	Let him
	He, the	Lord of	armies,	
to his	Son, Jesus	Christ, the	Lord,	to the

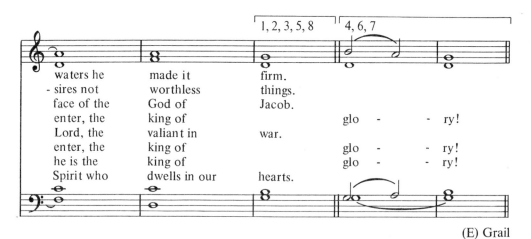

1, 2, 3, 5, 8   4, 6, 7

waters he	made it	firm.		
- sires not	worthless	things.		
face of the	God of	Jacob.		
enter, the	king of		glo -	- ry!
Lord, the	valiant in	war.		
enter, the	king of		glo -	- ry!
he is the	king of		glo -	- ry!
Spirit who	dwells in our	hearts.		

(E) Grail

22 Psalm 118(119)

India
Christopher Coelho 1968

a 4 Refrain

1. Your word, O Lord, is a lamp to my feet,— a light on my path. —

Verses

1.	I will ponder	all	your	precepts:
2.	I am a pil - - -	grim	on	earth:
3.	The law of your mouth means	more	to	me
4.	Your word, O	Lord	for	ever
5.	Had your law not been	my	de -	light
6.	You are my shel - -	ter,	my	shield;
7.	The unfolding of your	word	gives	light:

and consi - - der your paths.
show to me your com - mands.
than sil - - - ver or gold.
stands firm in the heavens.
I would have died in my af - fliction.
I hope in your word.
and teach - - - es the simple.

Open my eyes that I may see
My soul lies in the dust;
Let your love come to me and I shall live,
Your truth lasts from age to age:
Your promise is sweeter to my taste
If you uphold me by your promise I shall live:
The justice of your will is e - ternal:

the wonders of your law.
by your word re - vive me.
for your law is my de - light.
like the earth you cre - ated.
than honey in the mouth.
let my hope be not in vain.
if you teach me I shall live.

43

23 Psalm 24 (25)

India
Christopher Coelho 1968

Unison Refrain

Re-mem-ber me, O Lord, re-mem-ber me, O

Lord, when you come_in-to your king-dom, when you come_ in-to your

king-dom, re-mem-ber me, __ Re-mem-ber me. 1. To you O Lord I

lift up my soul, I trust you, let me not be dis-ap-point-

-ed. Lord, make me know your ways, Lord teach me your paths. Re-mem-ber 2. Make me walk in your truth and teach me, for

you are my God, my Sa-viour; in you I hope all the day long, be-

-cause of your good-ness O Lord. Re-mem-ber 3. Do not re-mem-ber the

[continued overleaf

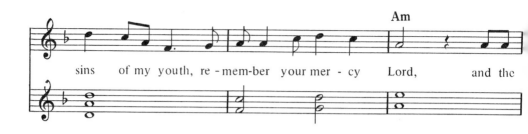

sins   of my youth, re-mem-ber your mer - cy   Lord,   and the

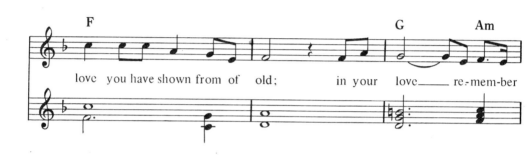

love you have shown from of   old;   in your   love____ re-mem-ber

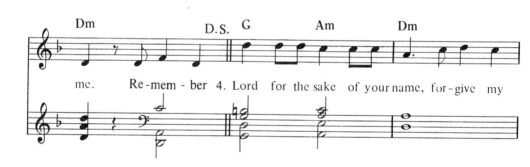

me.   Re-mem - ber 4. Lord for the sake of your name, for-give my

guilt___ for it is   great.   Turn   to me and have mer - cy for I am

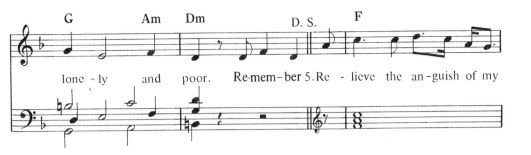

lone - ly and poor. Re-mem-ber 5.Re - lieve the an-guish of my

heart and set me free __ from my dis - tress. See my af-flic-tion and my

toil and take all my sins a - way. Re-mem- ber

24 Psalm 102 (103)

France
Antienne: J. Langlais 1953
Psalmodie: J. Gelineau 1953

Antienne

Le Sei - gneur est ten - dresse et pi - tié, lent
For the Lord is com - pas - sion and love, slow to

à la co - lè - re et plein d'a - mour.
an - ger and rich in mer - cy.

Versets

1. Bé - nis le Sei - gneur, ô mon âme, et du fond de mon
2. Lui qui par - donne toutes tes of - fenses, qui te gué - rit de
3. Le Sei - gneur qui fait œuvre de ju - stice, qui fait droit à
4. Le Sei - gneur est ten - dresse et pi - tié, lent à la co -

être, son saint nom, bé - nis le Sei - gneur, ô mon âme,
toute ma - la - die, qui ra - chète à la fos - se ta vie,
tous les op - pri - més, révé - la ses des - seins à Mo - ïse,
- lère et plein d'a - mour; elle n'est pas jusqu'à la fin, sa que - relle;

n'ou - blic au - cun de ses bien- faits. *(fin)*
qui te cou - ronne d'a - mour et de ten- dresse, qui rassa - sie de
aux en - fants d'Isra - ël, ses hauts - faits. *(fin)*
elle n'est pas pour tou- jours, sa ran - cune; il n'agit pas envers

2. biens tes a - nnées, et ta jeu - nesse comme l'aigle se renou - velle.
4. nous selon nos fautes, ne nous rend pas se - lon nos of - fenses.

Verses

1. My soul, give thanks to the Lord, all my being,
2. It is he who for - gives all your guilt, who heals every
3. The Lord does deeds of justice gives judgment for
4. The Lord is com - passion and love, slow to anger and

bless his ho - ly name. My soul, give thanks to the Lord
one of your ills, who re - deems your life from the grave,
all who are op - pressed. He made known his ways to Moses
rich in___ mercy. His wrath will come to an end,

[continued overleaf

49

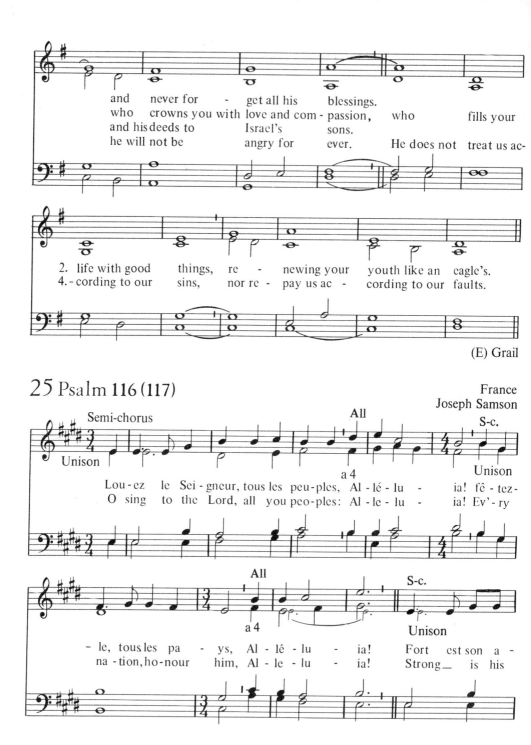

and never for - get all his blessings.
who crowns you with love and com - passion, who fills your
and his deeds to Israel's sons.
he will not be angry for ever. He does not treat us ac-

2. life with good things, re - newing your youth like an eagle's.
4. - cording to our sins, nor re - pay us ac - cording to our faults.

(E) Grail

25 Psalm 116 (117)

France
Joseph Samson

Semi-chorus   All   S-c.

Unison   Unison
a 4

Lou - ez le Sei - gneur, tous les peu - ples, Al - lé - lu - ia! fê - tez-
O sing to the Lord, all you peo - ples: Al - le - lu - ia! Ev' - ry

All   S-c.

a 4   Unison

- le, tous les pa - ys, Al - lé - lu - ia! Fort est son a -
na - tion, ho - nour him, Al - le - lu - ia! Strong— is his

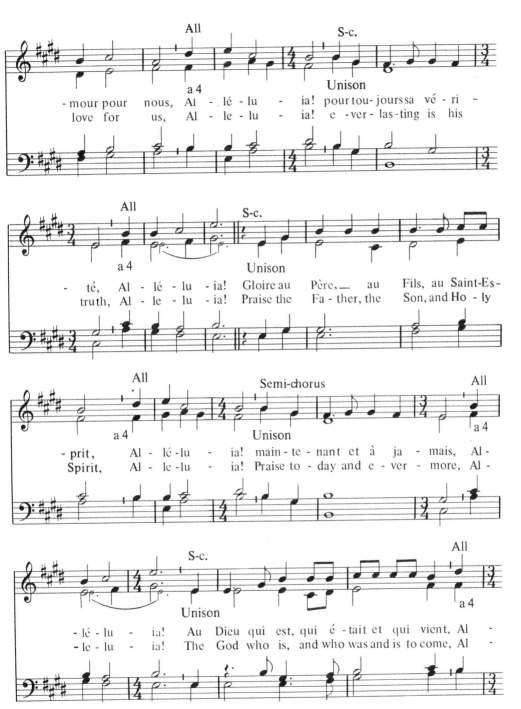

-mour pour nous, Al - lé - lu - ia! pour tou-jours sa vé - ri -
love for us, Al - le - lu - ia! e - ver - las-ting is his

- té, Al - lé - lu - ia! Gloire au Père, — au Fils, au Saint-Es-
truth, Al - le - lu - ia! Praise the Fa - ther, the Son, and Ho - ly

- prit, Al - lé - lu - ia! main - te - nant et à ja - mais, Al -
Spirit, Al - le - lu - ia! Praise to - day and e - ver - more, Al -

- lé - lu - ia! Au Dieu qui est, qui é - tait et qui vient, Al -
- le - lu - ia! The God who is, and who was and is to come, Al -

[continued overleaf

51

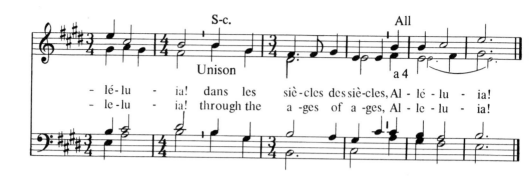

- lé-lu - ia! dans les siè-cles des siè-cles, Al - lé - lu - ia!
- le-lu - ia! through the a -ges of a -ges, Al - le - lu - ia!

26 Psalm 129 (130)

France
J. Gelineau 1953

Je mets mon es - poir dans le Sei -
I place all my trust in you my

- gneur, je suis sûr de sa pa - ro - le!
God: all my hope is in your sa - ving Word.

Versets

1. Des profon - deurs, je crie vers toi, Sei - gneur: é -
2. Si tu re - tiens les fautes, Sei - gneur, qui
3. Mon âme at - tend le Sei - gneur, je suis
4. Puisqu'au - près du Sei - gneur est la grâce, l'abon -
5. (Gloire au Père, au Fils, au Saint-Es - prit, mainte -

- coute mon ap - pel! Que ton o - reille se fasse atten -
donc sub-sis - te - ra? Mais près de toi se trouve le par -
sûr de sa pa - role; mon âme at - tend plus sûre - ment le Sei -
- dance du ra - chat, c'est lui qui rachète - ra Isra -
- nant et à ja - mais; au Dieu qui est, qui é - tait et qui

- tive au cri de ma pri - è - re.
- don: je te crains et j'es - pè - re.
- gneur qu'un veil - leur n'at -tend l'au - ro - re.
- ël de tou - tes ses fau - tes.
vient dans les siè - cles des siè - cles.)

Verses

1. Out of the depths I cry to you, O Lord,
2. If you, O Lord, should mark our guilt,
3. My soul is waiting for the Lord, I
4. Be - cause with the Lord there is mercy and
5. To the Father Al - mighty give glory, give

[continued overleaf

Lord,	hear my	voice!	O	let your	ears be at -
Lord, who	would sur -	vive?	But with	you is	found for -
count	on his	word:	My	soul is	longing for the
fullness	of re -	demption,		Israel in -	deed he will re-
glory	to his	Son,	to the	Spirit most	Holy give

- tentive	to the	voice	of my	plead -	ing.
- giveness:	for	this	we re -	vere	you.
Lord	more than a	watch -	man for	day -	break.
- deem	from	all	its in -	iqui -	ty.
praise,	whose	reign	is for	ev -	er.

(E) Grail

27 Psalm 135 (136)

France
J. Gelineau 1953

Unison Solo   All

1. Ren - dez grâce au Sei - gneur il est bon,
2. Lui seul a fait des mer-veilles, ⎫
3. Il a fait les grands lu - mi -naires, ⎬ Car é-ter-nel
4. Il frap-pa les premiers - nés des E - gyp-tiens, ⎭

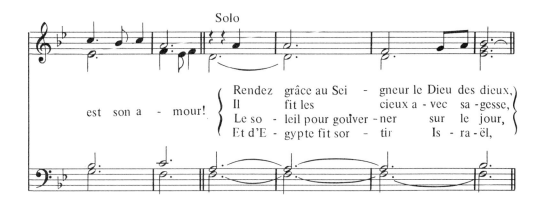

Solo

est son a - mour!

Rendez grâce au Sei - gneur le Dieu des dieux,
Il fit les cieux a - vec sa -gesse,
Le so - leil pour gouver -ner sur le jour,
Et d'E - gypte fit sor - tir Is - ra -ël,

All

Solo

Car é - ter - nel est son a -mour!

Rendez grâce au Sei -
Il affer - mit la
La lune et les é -
A main forte et à

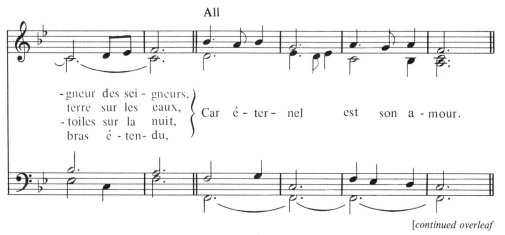

All

-gneur des sei - gneurs,
terre sur les eaux,
-toiles sur la nuit,
bras é - ten- du,

Car é - ter - nel est son a - mour.

[continued overleaf

5. Il fen - dit la mer Rouge en deux parts,
6. Il me - na son peuple au dé - sert,
7. Il don - na leur terre en hé - ri - tage,
8. Il nous sau - va de la main des op-pres-seurs, } Car é - ter - nel

est son a - mour!

Et fit pas-ser Isra - ël en son mi - lieu,
Il frap - pa des prin - ces puis-sants,
En héri-tage à Isra - ël son ser - vi - teur,
A toute chair il don - ne le pain, }

Car é -ter - nel est son a - mour!

Y culbu - tant Phara -
Fit pé - rir des
Il se sou - vint de son
Rendez grâce au Dieu du

56

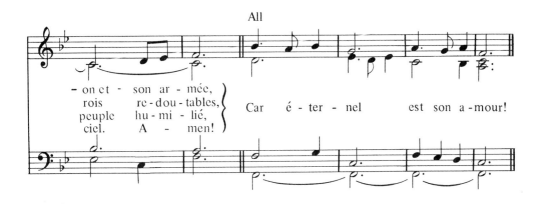

- on et - son ar - mée,
rois re - dou - tables,
peuple hu - mi - lié,
ciel. A - men!

Car é - ter - nel est son a - mour!

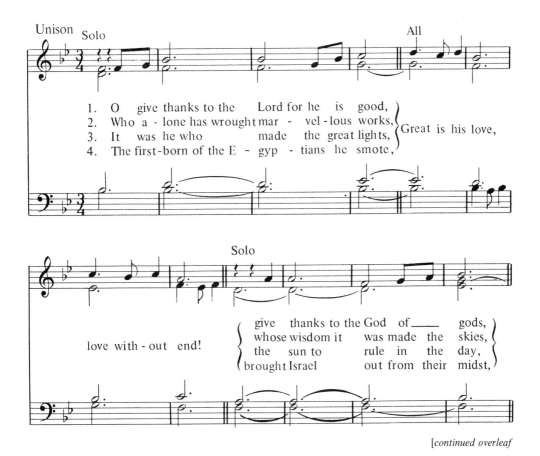

Unison Solo

1. O give thanks to the Lord for he is good,
2. Who a - lone has wrought mar - vel - lous works,
3. It was he who made the great lights,
4. The first - born of the E - gyp - tians he smote,

Great is his love,

All

love with - out end!

give thanks to the God of ____ gods,
whose wisdom it was made the skies,
the sun to rule in the day,
brought Israel out from their midst,

Solo

[*continued overleaf*

Great is his love,   love with-out   end!

give   thanks to the
who   fixed the earth
the   moon and
arm out -stretched, with

Lord   of __ lords,
firmly on the seas,
stars   in the night,
power   in his hand,

Great   is   his   love,   love with-out end!

5.   He   di- vided the   Red   Sea in   two,
6. Through the desert his   peo - ple he led,
7.   He   let Israel in -   he - rit their land,
8.   And   he snatched us a - way from our foes,

Great is his love,

give thanks to the God of__ gods,
nations in their great - ness he struck,
on his servants their land he bes-towed,
he gives food to all li - ving things,

love with - out end!

All

Great is his love, love with-out end!

Solo

give thanks to the
kings in their
he re - membered
to the God of

All

Lord of__ lords,
splen - dour he slew.
us in our dis-tress,
hea - ven give thanks,

Great is his love, love with-out end!

28 Psalm 150

India
Charles Mani (Tamil)

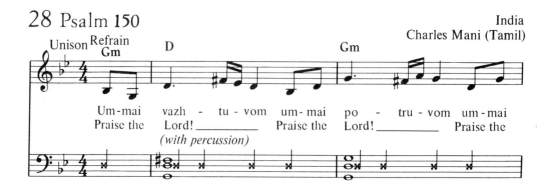

Um-mai vazh - tu - vom um-mai po - tru - vom um-mai
Praise the Lord! _____ Praise the Lord! _____ Praise the
(with percussion)

e - thu - vom_ i - rai - va um- mai e - thu - vom_ i - rai -
Lord on_earth and in the_ heav'ns: let all things that breathe praise the_

simile

- va - va.
Lord! Lord!

[continued overleaf

2. Ek ka - la tho - ni - yu - da - ne nam
2. Praise him with trum - pet's ro - yal_ sound: with

i - rai - va nai po - tru vom. vom
lute and harp and zi - ther praise his name! name!

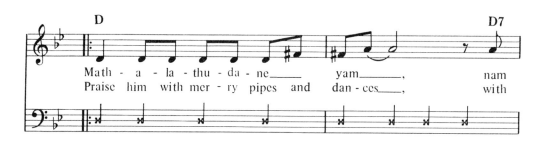

Math - a - la - thu - da - ne_____ yam_____, nam
Praise him with mer - ry pipes and dan - ces____, with

i - rai - va - nai e - thu - vom. — vom.
drum and__ ta - bor beat out his praise. praise.

3. Ya - zho-dum vi - nai - yo - dum pul - lan - gu-zha-lo-dum
3. Cym-bals high: cym - bals clang-ing: praise your cre-a - tor's name!

Ya - zho - -dum nam i - rai - va - nai____ po - tru-vom.
Cym-bals name! Let ev'rything that hath breath praise the Lord!

In performance the Refrain should be sung by all, the verses by a soloist or group. Percussion instruments or hand-clapping should be used to accompany throughout; a melodic instrument or group playing in unison at different pitches can insert the interludes. Harmony can be used in the Refrain as indicated, but should not be attempted in the verses.

The Human Condition
Das Leben des Menschen
La Condition Humaine

29

England
Henry Purcell 1659—1695

a 4 **Westminster Abbey**

1. God of grace and__ God of glo - ry,__ on thy peo - ple

pour__ thy__ power; now ful - fil thy__ Church-'s sto - ry,

Bring her bud____ to glo - rious flower. Grant us wis - dom,

grant us cour - age, for the fac - ing of ____ this ____ hour.

2. Lo, the hosts of evil round us / scorn thy Christ, assail his ways; / from the fears that long have bound us / free our hearts to faith and praise. / Grant us wisdom, grant us courage, / for the facing of this hour.

3. Cure thy children's warring madness, / bend our pride to thy control; / shame our wanton, selfish gladness, / rich in goods and poor in soul, / grant us wisdom, grant us courage, / lest we miss thy kingdom's goal.

4. Set our feet on lofty places, / gird our lives that they may be / armoured with all Christ-like graces / in the fight to set men free. / Grant us wisdom, grant us courage, / that we fail not man nor thee.

Harry Emerson Fosdick 1930

U.S.A.
Nick Hodson
Harm. Erik Routley 1975

1. It's a long, hard journey, and the road keeps turning and we just keep tra-vel-ling on;____ the signs aren't clear enough, the ends aren't near e-nough, and half our time__ is gone. O, the Lord sends trou-bles, the Lord sends tri-als, the

Lord sends a hea-vy — load. But he'll keep on lead-ing us and keep on guid-ing us as long as we're trav' - ling his road, — as long as we're trav' - ling his road.

2. With so many days to live, it's hard for life to give a meaning mile after mile. / The roads keep crossing, and the coins we're tossing choose the path in a visionless style. / O, the Lord . . .

3. Though we walk as brothers, still we hurt each other, and our love turns acid and stone. / Though we're hand in hand we don't understand that no one's walking alone. / O, the Lord . . .

4. Well, he never told us that the road before us would be smooth or simple or clear. / But he set us singing and our hope keeps springing and we're raised from hating and fear. / O, the Lord . . .

5. Well, the road is ours with its rocks and flowers and mica gleams in the stone. / Well, there's joy awaiting in the celebrating that we're never walking alone. / O, the Lord . . .

Nick Hodson

Jamaican Folk-song
arr. Doreen Potter 1972

Unison

1. Take the dark___ strength of our nights, soft with pee - ny
2. Take the pro - test of our need, what the gar - den?
3. Take the is - lands' hu - man skills, danc - ing seas___ and

wal - lies' lights. Take the star - signs wheel - ing round,
what the weed? Take the orb___ and break the chain,
wise old hills. Take our Je - sus and his power,

while the steel - drum melts to sound. Take and weave___ a
break the shack - les of the brain. Take and weave___ a
match his peo - ple to this hour. Take and weave___ a

womb of night___ that we may live___ that we may live.
womb of right___ that we may live___ that we may live.
womb of light___ that we may live___ that we may live.

John Hoad 1971

32

Germany
Hans-Rudolf Siemoneit 1965

1. Die gan - ze Welt hast du uns ü - ber -
1. You gave us all the world for our do -

- las - sen. Doch wir be - grei - fen dei - ne Groß - mut
- mi - nion, but such a gift we could not com - pre -

nicht. ___ Du gibst uns frei. Wir lau - fen eig - ne
- hend. ___ You set us free. We ran a - round in

[continued overleaf

We - ge | in die - sem un - er - mess - lich wei -
cir - cles | in this un - li - mi - ted ex - tent___

- ten Raum. Gott schenkt Frei - heit. Sei - ne größ - te
- of space. God gives free - dom; sends his great - est

Ga - be gibt er sei - nen Kin - dern. Kin - dern.___
gift to please his a - dult chil - dren. chil - dren.___

Last time

70

2. Du läßt in deiner Liebe uns gewähren. / Dein Name ist unendliche Geduld. / Und wir sind frei, zu hoffen und zu glauben, / und wir sind frei, zu Trotz und Widerstand. / Gott schenkt Freiheit. Seine größte Gabe gibt er seinen Kindern.

3. Wir wollen leben und uns selbst behaupten. / Doch deine Freiheit setzen wir aufs Spiel. / Nach unserm Willen soll die Welt sich ordnen, / wir bauen selbstgerecht den Turm der Zeit. / Gott schenkt Freiheit. Seine größte Gabe gibt er seinen Kindern.

4. Wir richten Mauern auf, wir setzen Grenzen / und wohnen hinter Gittern unsrer Angst. / Wir sind nur Menschen, die sich fürchten können, / wir brachten selbst uns in Gefangenschaft. / Gott schenkt Freiheit. Seine größte Gabe gibt er seinen Kindern.

5. Wenn du uns richtest, Herr, sind wir verloren. / Auf unsern Schultern lastet schwere Schuld. / Laß deine Gnade, Herr, vor Recht ergehen; / von gestern und von morgen sprich uns los. / Gott schenkt Freiheit. Seine größte Gabe gibt er seinen Kindern.

6. Gib uns die Wege frei, die zu dir führen, / denn uns verlangt nach deinem guten Wort. / Du machst uns frei zu lieben und zu hoffen, / das gibt uns Zuversicht für jeden Tag. / Gott schenkt Freiheit. Seine größte Gabe gibt er seinen Kindern.

Christa Weiss 1964

2. In love, you leave us to our own devices, / whilst your eternal patience suffers long. / And we are free in hoping and believing, / and we are free to trust and to resist. / God gives freedom; sends his greatest gift to please his adult children.

3. We want to live and make our own decisions / but yours the freedom that we put at stake. / We think the world revolves around our wishes; / self-righteously we build the tower of time. / God gives freedom; sends his greatest gift to please his adult children.

4. We build up walls, inventing dismal frontiers, / and live behind the iron bars of fear. / We know this fear because we are but human; / we brought ourselves into captivity. / God gives freedom; sends his greatest gift to please his adult children.

5. If you should judge us, Lord, we are in error. / We're burdened with a sense of heavy guilt. / Let grace have precedence of legal justice; / acquit us daily from the sentence due. / God gives freedom; sends his greatest gift to please his adult children.

6. Make free for us the way that leads towards you, / because we long to hear your gracious Word. / You make us free in loving and in hoping, / which gives us confidence to greet each day. / God gives freedom; sends his greatest gift to please his adult children.

John B. Geyer 1971

33

Sweden
Sven-Eric Johanson 1968

Unison

Em · Am · Em

1. 'Vi vil - le dig se', så gre - ker - na bad, och
1. 'It's Je - sus we want', re - quest - ed the Greeks, and

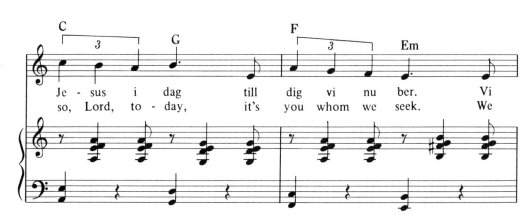

C · G · F · Em

Je - sus i dag till dig vi nu ber. Vi
so, Lord, to - day, it's you whom we seek. We

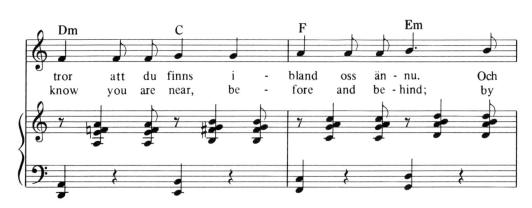

Dm · C · F · Em

tror att du finns i - bland oss än - nu. Och
know you are near, be - fore and be - hind; by

kans-ke vårt liv är du, ba-ra du._____
you, on-ly you, cre-a - tion is signed.____

2. I strömmen av liv, i gatornas brus / vi skymtar ibland ditt ansiktes ljus; / en gråt och ett skrik ur ångestens djup, / då rycker vi till; vi hör det är du.

3. Vi tror du är med bland dem som för fred / och frihet och rätt mot bergen sej drar, / till djungel och skog, vår broder och vän / tills jorden igen är mänskornas hem.

4. O sårade kropp som aldrig kan dö, / o kärlek som högt på ett kors spikas opp, / du eviga ljus och skapade ord, / låt frihetens träd gå i blom på vår jord.

Anders Frostenson 1971

2. Sometimes in the streets of hurry and haste, / we happen to catch the light of your face; / a cry and a shout from deepest despair. / We stop and we know: it's you whom we hear.

3. We know that you live in jungle and wood / with those who are bent on freedom's pursuit. / You take to the hills, their brother and friend, / till earth is again a home for mankind.

4. Rejected by men and nailed to a cross, / you die but you rise for ever with us. / You, light of the age, and formative word, / let freedom spring up and blossom on earth!

Fred Kaan 1972

34

Scotland
Reginald Barrett-Ayres 1966

Unison

1. 'Am I my brother's keeper?' The

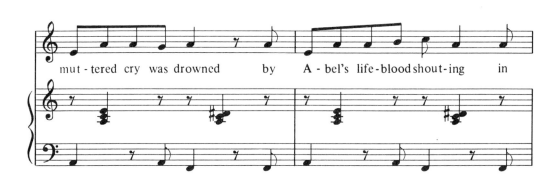

mut - tered cry was drowned by A - bel's life-blood shout-ing in

si - lence from the ground. For no man is an is - land di -

-vi - ded from the main; the bell that toll'd for A - bel toll'd

e - qual - ly for Cain. (3) hands.

after verse 3

2. The ruler called for water / and thought his hands were clean. / Christ counted less than order / the man than the machine. / The crowd cried 'Crucify him!' / their malice wouldn't budge, / so Pilate called for water / and history's his judge.

3. As long as people hunger, / as long as people thirst, / and ignorance and illness / and warfare do their worst, / as long as there's injustice / in any of God's lands, / I am my brother's keeper, / I dare not wash my hands.

John Ferguson 1966

35

Brazil
João Wilson Faustini 1967
Harm. C.D.

Unison In well-defined rhythm. With majesty.

1. Nes - ta gran - de ci - da - de vi - ve - mos on - de
1. Mo - dern man has the ci - ty for his home _____ where his

mui - tos es - tão ___ a lu - tar, en - tre a in -
life is walled in by want and dread, pained by

- sō - nia e o tra - ba - lho cons - tan - - te pa - ra o
nights with - out sleep and days of grind - ing work, in the

pão co - ti - dia - no ga - nhar.
strug - gle to earn his dai - ly bread.

2. Nesta grande cidade que cresce / há milhares sem fé, sem amor, / que precisam da graça de Cristo / p'ra viver uma vida melhor.

3. Nesta grande e ruidosa cidade / há milhares sedentos de luz, / multidões sem ouvir a mensagem / do poder salvador de Jesus.

4. Nesta grande cidade onde há crimes, / onde há fome, dinheiro, ilusão . . . / nós, os filhos de Deus fomos postos / como luz, a indicar salvação.

5. Cresce, cresce, cidade gigante, / crescem fábricas e arranha-céus, / mas não podes crescer desprezando / o evangelho do Cristo de Deus!

João Dias de Araujo 1967

2. In our cities, immense and growing out, / there are millions from faith and love estranged, / who need to recapture hope of better things, / and whose hearts, by the grace of Christ, can change.

3. In the dark of our noisy city life, / men and women are groping for the light, / human beings who hunger to see right prevail, / unaware of the liberating Christ.

4. In the great giant cities of our globe, / hollowed out by the ways of greed and crime, / we are set to reflect the likeness of our God / and to act out renewal's great design.

5. Grow then, cities, to house the world of man, / with your skyscrapers blotting out the sun. / Let Christ be the light to shine from human homes / in the high-rising blocks of steel and stone.

Fred Kaan 1972

Anguilla

Jamaica
Doreen Potter 1972

Unison Eb

1. Can I see the suffer-ing crowd and not lend a hand? Can I hear the hung-ry cry and fail to un-der-stand? Can the beg-gar's out-stretched hand fail to call forth a re-sponse? Then stir my heart, O Lord, then stir my heart.

2. Can I see the heav-y la-den and not help bear the load? Can I hear the deep-est sigh or bro-ken heart-ed groan? Can I hear the cry for help and pass un-heed-ing by? Then stir my heart, O Lord, then stir my heart.

3. Hand and heart I give you Lord, and not lip ser-vice to a creed, may I bring new hope and joy to a world of need; may my days on earth in ser-vice to my fel-low-men be spent; so stir my heart, O Lord, so stir my heart.

S. Wilfred Hodge 1972

England
Sydney Carter 1962
Harm. C.D.

1. When I need - ed a neighbour were you there, were you there? When I need - ed a neigh-bour were you there? And the creed and the co-lour and the name won't mat-ter, were you there?

2. I was hungry and thirsty, were you there, were you there? . . .

3. I was cold, I was naked, were you there, were you there? . . .

4. When I needed a healer were you there, were you there? . . .

5. Wherever you travel I'll be there, I'll be there, . . .

And the creed and the colour and the name won't matter, I'll be there.

Sydney Carter 1962

Jamaica
Doreen Potter 1970

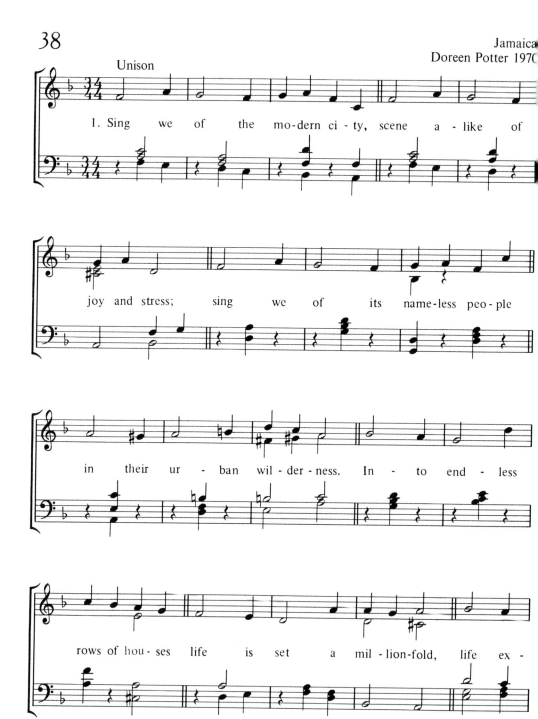

Unison

1. Sing we of the mo-dern ci-ty, scene a-like of joy and stress; sing we of its name-less peo-ple in their ur-ban wil-der-ness. In-to end-less rows of hou-ses life is set a mil-lion-fold, life ex-

- pressed in hu - man be - ings dai - ly born and grow-ing old.

2. In the city full of people, world of speed and hectic days; / in the ever changing setting of the latest trend and craze, / Christ is present and among us, in the crowd we see him stand. / In the bustle of the city Jesus Christ is everyman.

3. God is not remote in heaven but on earth to share our shame; / changing graph and mass and numbers into persons with a name. / Christ has shown, beyond statistics, human life with glory crowned; / by his timeless presence proving: people matter, people count!

Fred Kaan 1968

39

Jamaica
Doreen Potter 1970

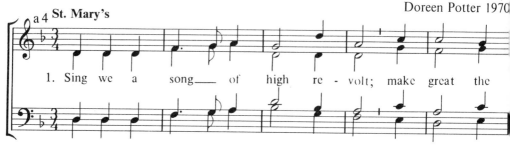

1. Sing we a song of high re - volt; make great the

Lord, his name ex - alt! Sing we the song that

Ma - ry sang, of God at war with hu - man wrong.

2. Sing we of him who deeply cares / and still with us our burden bears. / He who with strength the proud disowns, / brings down the mighty from their thrones.

3. By him the poor are lifted up; / he satisfies with bread and cup / the hungry men of many lands; / the rich must go with empty hands.

4. He calls us to revolt and fight / with him for what is just and right, / to sing and live 'Magnificat' / in crowded street and council flat.

Fred Kaan 1968

40a

France
Philibert Jambe-de-Fer 1555

a 3 **Lyon 59**

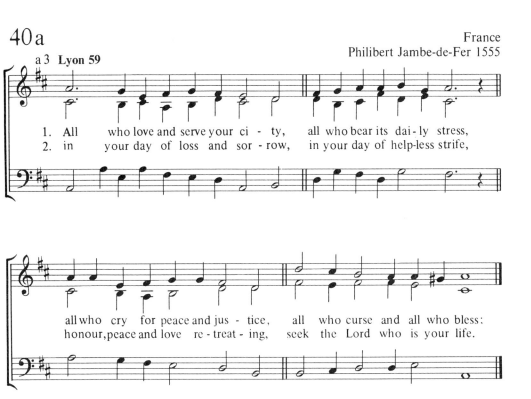

1. All who love and serve your ci - ty, all who bear its dai - ly stress,
2. in your day of loss and sor - row, in your day of help-less strife,

all who cry for peace and jus - tice, all who curse and all who bless:
honour, peace and love re - treat - ing, seek the Lord who is your life.

3. In your day of wealth and plenty, / wasted work and wasted play, / call to mind the word of Jesus, / 'I must work while it is day.'

4. For all days are days of judgment, / and the Lord is waiting still, / drawing near to men who spurn him, / offering peace from Calvary's hill.

5. Risen Lord! shall yet the city / be the city of despair? / Come today, our Judge, our Glory, / be its name, 'The Lord is there!'

Erik Routley 1966

83

40 b

England
Peter Cutts 1961

Unison **Birabus** (alternative tune, Music Edition only)

1. All who love and serve your ci - ty, all who
2. in your day of loss and sor - row, in your

bear its dai - ly stress, all who cry for peace and
day of help - less strife, ho - nour, peace and love re -

attacca

jus - tice, all who curse and all who bless;
- treat - ing, seek the Lord who is your life.

3. In your day of wealth and plenty, / wasted work and wasted play, /
call to mind the word of Jesus, / 'I must work while it is day.'

4. For all days are days of judgment, / and the Lord is waiting still, /
drawing near to men who spurn him, / offering peace from Calvary's hill.

5. Risen Lord! shall yet the city / be the city of despair? / Come today,
our Judge, our Glory, / be its name, 'The Lord is there!'

Erik Routley 1966

84

41 King's Lynn

Unison

1. O God of earth and al - tar, bow— down and hear our cry; our—
earth-ly ru - lers— fal - ter, our peo - ple drift and die; the—
walls of gold en - tomb us, the swords of scorn di - vide; take
not thy thun - der from— us, but— take a - way our pride.

[vv. 2, 3 overleaf

2. From all that terror teaches, from lies of tongue and pen, / from all the easy speeches that comfort cruel men; / from sale and profanation of honour and the sword; / from sleep and from damnation, deliver us, good Lord!

3. Tie in a living tether the prince and priest and thrall, / bind all our lives together: smite us and save us all! / In ire and exultation, aflame with faith and free, / lift up a living nation, a single sword to thee!

G. K. Chesterton 1874–1936

42 **Old 124th**

Switzerland
Octante-trois Pseaumes, Geneva 1551
English form of melody Harm. W. Parsons 1563

1. Turn back, O man, for-swear thy fool-ish ways. Old now is earth, and none may count her days, yet thou her child, whose head is crowned with flame, still wilt not hear thine in-ner God pro-

-claim: 'Turn back, O man, for - swear thy fool - ish_____ ways.'

2. Earth might be fair, and all men glad and wise. / Age after age their tragic empires rise, / built while they dream, and in that dreaming weep: / would man but wake from out his haunted sleep, / earth might be fair and all men glad and wise.

3. Earth shall be fair, and all her people one; / nor till that hour shall God's whole will be done. / Now, even now, once more from earth to sky, / peals forth in joy man's old undaunted cry. / 'Earth shall be fair, and all her people one.'

Clifford Bax 1916

God's Promises and Providence
Gottes Verheißung und Vorsehung
Les Promesses de Dieu et sa Providence

England
Geoffrey Laycock 1971

43 **Harvest**

Unison

1. Now join we to praise the Cre - a - tor our voi - ces in wor - ship and song; we stand to re - call with thanks - giv - ing that to him all sea - sons be - long.

2. We thank you O God for your goodness, / for the joy and abundance of crops; / for food that is stored in our larders, / for all we can buy in the shops.

3. But also of need and starvation / we sing with concern and despair, / of skills that are used for destruction, / of land that is burnt and laid bare.

4. We cry for the plight of the hungry, / while harvests are left on the field, / for orchards neglected and wasting, / for produce from markets withheld.

5. The song grows in depth and in wideness; / the earth and its people are one. / There can be no thanks without giving, / no words without deeds that are done.

6. Then teach us, O Lord of the harvest, / to be humble in all that we claim; / to share what we have with the nations, / to care for the world in your name.

Fred Kaan 1968

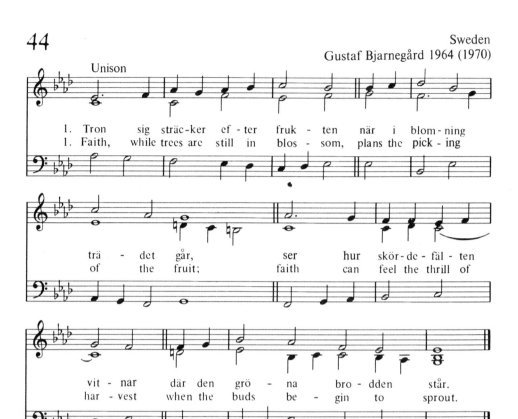

Unison

1. Tron   sig sträc-ker ef - ter fruk - ten när i blom - ning
1. Faith,   while trees are still in blos - som, plans the pick - ing

trä - det går,   ser hur skör- de - fäl - ten
of   the   fruit;   faith can feel the thrill of

vit - nar där den grö - na bro - dden står.
har - vest when the buds be - gin to sprout.

2. Innan gryningsljuset ännu / över bergen tänds i brand, / skådar tron den nya dagen / hastar till sin gärning fram.

3. Länge förrän regnet kommit, / hördes Noas hammarslag. / Bortom främlingskap och träldom / Abraham såg Kristi dag.

4. Innan vattnet ännu delats, / lyfte tron sin stav och såg / hur en väg på havets botten / framför Israels fötter låg.

5. Tro är visshet om Guds löfte, / ting som inte syns men finns / svarar honom som oss kallar: / 'Ja, jag kommer. Ja, jag vill'.

Anders Frostenson 1960

2. Long before the dawn is breaking, / faith anticipates the sun. / Faith is eager for the daylight, / for the work that must be done.

3. Long before the rains were coming, / Noah went and built an ark. / Abraham, the lonely migrant, / saw the Light beyond the dark.

4. Faith, uplifted, tamed the water / of the undivided sea / and the people of the Hebrews / found the path that made them free.

5. Faith believes that God is faithful. / - He will be that he will be - / Faith accepts his call, responding: / 'I am willing: Lord, send me.'

Fred Kaan 1972

England
Erik Routley 1971
Composed for C.D.

Corbridge

1. God _____ who spoke in the be - gin - ning form - ing rock and
sha - ping spar, set _____ all life and growth in mo - tion,
earth - ly world and dis - tant star; he who calls the
earth to or - der is the ground of what_____ we are.

2. God who spoke through men and nations, / through events long past
and gone; / showing still today his purpose, / speaks supremely through
his Son; / He who calls the earth to order / gives his word and it is done.

3. God whose speech becomes incarnate, / – Christ is servant, Christ is
Lord! – / calls us to a life of service, / heart and will to action stirred; /
He who uses man's obedience / has the first and final word.

Fred Kaan 1968

France
Joseph Gelineau 1966

1. Pè - re du pre-mier mot jail - li   dans le pre-mier si -
1. Fa - ther of that pri - me -val word   which burst forth from the

- len - ce   où l'homme a com-men - cé,   en - tends mon - ter vers
si - lence, where man   al -so took form,   hear,   ri - sing up like

toi   comme en é - cho,   nos   voix   mê -lées aux
e - choes from the   earth,   our   voi - ces sing - ing

chants que lan - ce____ ton Bien-Ai - mé. (3)__ ton Pre-mier - né.
songs that first_your__ Be - lo-ved   sang. (3)__your first-born   Son.

2. Père du premier jour / levé sur les premières terres / au souffle de l'Esprit, / voici devant tes yeux / comme en retour, / le feu / qui prend au coeur des frères / de Jésus Christ.

3. Pére du premier fruit / gonflé de la première sève / au monde ensemencé, / reçois le sang des grains / qui ont mûri, / et viens / remplir les mains qui cherchent / ton Premier-né.

Didier Rimaud

2. Father of that primeval day your Spirit's breath enkindled / across the new-made lands, / see now, as if reflected from that dawn, / the fire which glows within the brothers of Jesus Christ.

3. Father of that primeval fruit by the first sap expanded, / to stock your self-sown world, / receive as sacrifice your ripened grain / and come to fill the hands that seek now your first-born Son.

Caryl Micklem 1972

47

Germany
Rolf Schweizer 1963

Introduction (before v. 1 only)

Solo instrument

Keyboard

Refrain (return after each verse)

Unison

Sin -get dem Herrn ein neu - es Lied, denn er tut Wun - der.
Sing to the Lord a new__ song for he does won - ders.

Sin - get dem Herrn ein neu - es Lied, denn er tut

Sing to the Lord a new__ song, for he does

Verses

· Wun - der. 1. Er sie - get__ mit sei - ner

won - ders. 1. God tri - umphs__ for he is

(Last time)

(Last time)

[continued overleaf

Rech - ten und mit sei - nem hei - li - gen Arm; der
right - eous, and his sa - cred - ness is his strength; the

Herr läßt sein Heil ver - kün - di - gen, er of - fen -
Lord has de - clared his sa - ving power, he ev' - ry -

D.S.

D.S.

- bart   sei - ne   Ge - rech - tig - keit.___
- where   dis - plays his   right - eous - ness.___

2. Du meinst, Gott sei sehr verborgen, / seine Macht sei klein und gering? / Gott sähe nicht das, was dich bedrückt? / Sieh auf dein Leben, er hat es bewahrt!

3. Du kennst oftmals deinen Weg nicht, / und du weißt nicht recht, was du sollst. / Doch da schickt Gott dir Hilfe zu: / den einen Menschen, der dich gut versteht.

4. Du mußt nur zu sehen lernen, / wie er dich so väterlich führt; / auch heute gibt er dir seine Hand, / so greif doch zu und schlage sie nicht aus.

(Strophe 1 wiederholen)   Paulus Stein 1963

2. You think God is the Unknown One, / that his power is of small account? / That God can't see what oppresses you? / Look at your life, how he takes care of it.

3. Often you don't know his purpose, / or what is the right thing to do, / but God sends his help to everyone / who truly seeks to understand him well.

4. You must learn to see him only / as the Father who guides your life; / this very day he holds out his hand: / so seize it now and do not turn away.

(v. 1 may be repeated)   F. Pratt Green 1972

48

France
Joseph Gelineau 1971
Composed for C.D.

ge - wiß an je - dem neu - en Tag. - sang.
- - ver fails to greet us each new day. praise.

2. Noch will das Alte unsre Herzen quälen, / noch drückt uns böser Tage schwere Last; / ach, Herr, gib unsern aufgescheuchten Seelen das Heil, / für das du uns bereitet hast.

3. Und reichst du uns den schweren Kelch, den bittern, / des Leids, gefüllt bis an den höchsten Rand, / so nehmen wir ihn dankbar ohne Zittern / aus deiner guten und geliebten Hand.

4. Doch willst du uns noch einmal Freude schenken / an dieser Welt und ihrer Sonne Glanz, / dann woll'n wir des Vergangenen gedenken, / und dann gehört dir unser Leben ganz.

5. Wenn sich die Stille nun tief um uns breitet, / so lass uns hören jenen vollen Klang / der Welt, die unsichtbar sich um uns weitet, / all deiner Kinder hohen Lobgesang.

Dietrich Bonhoeffer 1944/5

2. Yet is this heart by its old foe tormented, / still evil days bring burdens hard to bear; / O give our frightened souls the sure salvation / for which, O Lord, you taught us to prepare.

3. And when this cup you give is filled to brimming / with bitter suffering, hard to understand, / we take it thankfully and without trembling / out of so good and so beloved a hand.

4. Yet when again, in this same world you give us / the joy we had, the brightness of your Sun, / we shall remember all the days we lived through / and our whole life shall then be yours alone.

5. Now when your silence deeply spreads around us, / O let us hear all your creation says: / That world of sound which soundlessly invades us, / and all your children's highest hymns of praise.

F. Pratt Green 1972

The original text by Dietrich Bonhoeffer is to be found in 'Dietrich Bonhoeffer, Widerstand und Ergebung', new ed. 1970, p. 435 f., Chr. Kaiser Verlag, Munich (English ed. 'Letters and Papers from Prison', SCM Press, London, and Macmillan). In the version reproduced here, vv. 1 and 5 of the original are omitted, while v. 7 of the original appears here as v. 1.

49

1. Guds kär - lek är som stran - den och som grä - set,
1. The love of God is broad like beach and mea - dow,

är__ vind och vidd och ett o - änd - ligt hem.
wide as the wind, and an e - ter - nal home.

Vi fri - het fick att bo där, gå och kom - ma,__
God leaves us free to seek him or re - ject him,__

att__ sä - ga 'ja' till Gud och sä - ga 'nej'.
he__ gives us room to an - swer 'yes' or 'no'.

Guds kär-lek är som stran-den och som grä-set,
The love of God is broad like beach and mea-dow,

är__ vind och vidd och ett o-änd-ligt hem.
wide as the wind, and an e-ter-nal home.

hem.
home.

Last verse

2. Vi vill den frihet där vi är oss själva, / den frihet vi kan göra något av, / som ej är tomhet men än rymd för drömmar, / en jord där träd och blommor kan slå rot. / Guds kärlek är som stranden och som gräset, / är vind och vidd och ett oändligt hem.

3. Och ändå är det murar oss emellan / och genom gallren ser vi på varann. / Vårt fängelse är byggt av rädslans stenar, / vår fångdräkt är vårt eget knutna jag. / Guds kärlek är som stranden och som gräset, / är vind och vidd och ett oändligt hem.

4. O, döm oss, Herre, frisäg oss i domen. / I din förlåtelse vår frihet är. / Den sträcker sig så långt din kärlek vandrar / bland alla mänskor, folk och raser här. / Guds kärlek är som stranden och som gräset, / är vind och vidd och ett oändligt hem.

Anders Frostenson 1968

2. We long for freedom where our truest being / is given hope and courage to unfold. / We seek in freedom space and scope for dreaming, / and look for ground where trees and plants may grow. / The love of God is broad like beach and meadow, / wide as the wind, and an eternal home.

3. But there are walls that keep us all divided; / we fence each other in with hate and war. / Fear is the bricks-and-mortar of our prison, / our pride of self the prison coat we wear. / The love of God is broad like beach and meadow, / wide as the wind, and an eternal home.

4. O, judge us, Lord, and in your judgment free us, / and set our feet in freedom's open space; / take us as far as your compassion wanders / among the children of the human race. / The love of God is broad like beach and meadow, / wide as the wind, and an eternal home.

Fred Kaan 1972

50

U.S.A.
James Carley 1969

Unison

1. When in his own im-age God cre - a - ted man,____

he in - clu - ded free-dom in cre - a - tion's plan.____

For he loved us e - ven from be - fore our birth; ____

by his grace____ he made us free - men_____ of this earth.

2. God to man entrusted life as gift and aim. / Sin became our prison, turning hope to shame. / Man against his brother lifted hand and sword, / and the father's pleading went unseen, unheard.

3. Then in time, our maker chose to intervene, / set his love in person in the human scene. / Jesus broke the circle of repeated sin, / so that man's devotion newly might begin.

4. Choose we now in freedom where we should belong, / let us turn to Jesus, let our choice be strong. / May the great obedience which in Christ we see / perfect all our service: then we shall be free!

Fred Kaan 1966

51

The Netherlands
Frits Mehrtens 1959

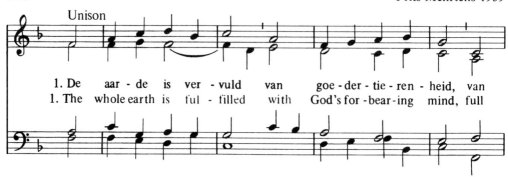

1. De aar - de is ver - vuld van goe - der - tie - ren - heid, van
1. The whole earth is ful - filled with God's for - bear - ing mind, full

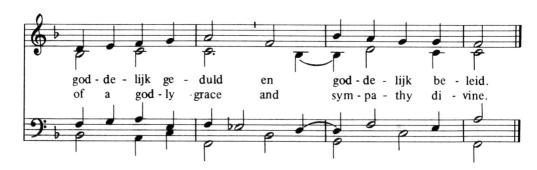

god - de - lijk ge - duld en god - de - lijk be - leid.
of a god - ly grace and sym - pa - thy di - vine.

2. Gods goedheid is te groot / voor het geluk alleen, / zij gaat in alle nood / door heel het leven heen.

3. Zij daalt als vruchtbaar zaad / tot in de groeve af / omdat zij niet verlaat / wie toeven in het graf.

4. Omdat zij niet vergeet / wie godverlaten zijn: / de wereld hemelsbreed / zal goede aarde zijn.

5. De sterren hemelhoog / zijn door dit zaad bereid / als dienaars tot de oogst / dergoedertierenheid.

6. Het zaad der goedheid Gods, / het hoge woord, de Heer, / valt in de voor des doods, / valt in de aarde neer.

7. Al gij die God bemint / en op zijn goedheid wacht, / de oogst ruist in de wind / als psalmen in de nacht.

W. Barnard 1970

2. God's goodness is too great / for happiness alone, / it goes through deepest pain, / bred in our very bone.

3. It penetrates as seed / into the furrow's womb / because it does not leave / the sleepers in the tomb.

4. Because it does not rest / until the lost are found, / sky-wide, the world becomes / a fair and fruitful ground.

5. The stars above, sky-high, / are by this seed prepared, / as servants sent to reap / the mercy of the Lord.

6. The seed of godly love, / the Lord, the world of truth, / descends into the earth, / into the soil of death.

7. All you, in love with God, / who for his goodness wait, / the grain waves in the wind / as psalmtunes in the night.

Fred Kaan 1972

52

Unison

1. De Heer heeft mij ge - zien en on - ver - wacht ben ik op-
1. The Lord has seen me, and to my sur- prise I'm like a

Organ

- nieuw ge - bo - ren en ge - to - gen. Hij heeft mijn licht ont -
child who's born and raised all o - ver. He set me glow - ing

- sto-ken in de nacht, gaf mij een le-vend hart en nieu-we o -
in the depths of night, my heart be - gan to beat, my eyes were o -

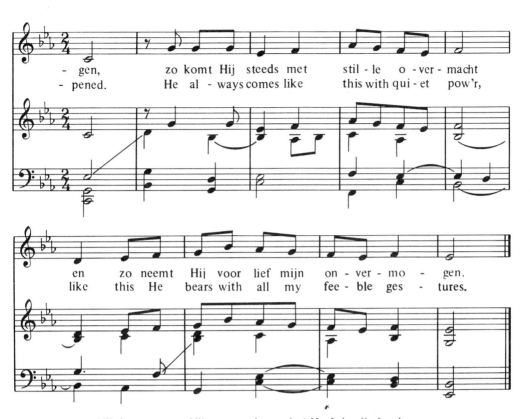

- gen, / zo komt Hij steeds met stil - le o - ver - macht
- pened. / He al - ways comes like this with qui - et pow'r,

en zo neemt Hij voor lief mijn on - ver - mo - gen.
like this He bears with all my fee - ble ges - tures.

2. Hij doet met ons, Hij gaat ons in en uit. / Heeft in zijn handen onze naam geschreven. / De Heer wil ons bewonen als zijn huis, / plant als een boom in ons zijn eigen leven, / wil met ons spelen neemt ons tot zijn bruid / en wat wij zijn, Hij heeft het ons gegeven.

3. Gij geeft het uw beminden in de slaap, / gij zaait uw naam in onze diepste dromen. / Gij hebt ons zelf ontvankelijk gemaakt / zoals de regen neerdaalt in de bomen, / zoals de wind, wie weet waarheen hij gaat, / zo zult Gij uw beminden overkomen.

Huub Oosterhuis

2. He deals with us, goes in and out of us. / Upon his hands our names are clearly written. / The Lord would dwell in us as in his house, / plant in us his life, a tree deep-rooted, / would play with us, and take us for his bride, / all that we are – the Lord alone has given.

3. You come to your belov'd when they're asleep, / implant your name like seed in our deep dreaming. / And you yourself have opened us to you / like rain descending on the thirsty tree-tops, / or like the wind – who knows where it may go? – / so shall you come upon your own beloved.

Redmond McGoldrick

Jesus Christ · His Advent and Incarnation
Jesus Christus · Ankunft und Menschwerdung
Jésus Christ · Avènement et Incarnation

53

Veni Emmanuel

France
Melody of uncertain date

Unison

1. Ve - ni, ve - ni Em - ma - - nu - el, cap - ti - vum sol - ve
1. O come, O come Im - ma - - nu - el, and ran - som cap - tive

Is - - ra - el, qui ge - mit in ex - si - - li - o
Is - - ra - el that mourns in lone - ly ex - - ile here

pri - va - tus De - i Fi - - li - o. Gau - de, gau - de! Em -
un - til the Son of God___ ap - pear. Re - joice! Re - joice! Im -

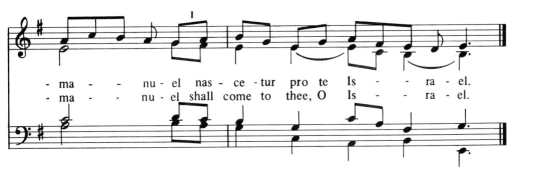

-ma - - nu - el nas - ce -tur pro te Is - - ra - el.
-ma - - nu - el shall come to thee, O Is - - ra - el.

2. Veni, O Jesse virgula, / ex hostis tuos ungula, / de specu tuos tartari / educ, et antro barathri. / Gaude, gaude, Emmanuel, / nascetur pro te, Israel.

3. Veni, veni O Oriens / solare nos adveniens, / noctis depelle nebulas / dirasque noctis tenebras. / Gaude, gaude, Emmanuel, / nascetur pro te, Israel.

4. Veni Clavis davidica, / regna reclude caelica, / fac iter tutum superum / et claude vias inferum. / Gaude, gaude, Emmanuel, / nascetur pro te, Israel.

18th century Latin tr.

2. O come, thou Rod of Jesse, free / thine own from Satan's tyranny. / From depths of hell thy people save / and give them vict'ry o'er the grave. / Rejoice! rejoice! Immanuel / shall come to thee, O Israel.

3. O come, thou dayspring, come and cheer / our spirits by thine advent here; / disperse the gloomy shades of night / and death's dark shadows put to flight. / Rejoice! rejoice! Immanuel / shall come to thee, O Israel.

4. O come, thou Key of David, come / and open wide our heavenly home; / make safe the way that leads on high, / and close the path to misery. / Rejoice! rejoice! Immanuel / shall come to thee, O Israel.

J. M. Neale 1852

54

France
Dominique Ombrie 1963

Refrain
a 4

Viens pour notre at - ten - te, ne tar - de ____ plus. Pour
Come to us who wait ____ here, and tar - ry ____ not! You

no - tre dé - li - vran - ce, viens, Sei - gneur ____ Jé - sus!
on - ly can de - li - ver us, Lord Je - sus.

Versets

1. Dans no - tre mon - de de dé - tres -
1. Out of our world, ____ out of its dis -

- se, nous t'ap - pe - lons, Sei - gneur Jé - sus.
- tress, we call on you, Lord Je - sus.

2. L'amour, plus fort que nos misères, / nous réunit, Seigneur Jésus.

3. Dans notre angoisse, nos ténèbres, / nous te cherchons, Seigneur Jésus.

4, Dans nos discordes qui te blessent, / nous t'implorons, Seigneur Jésus.

5. Tu es venu chez nous en pauvre / pour nous sauver, Seigneur Jésus.

6. Ta Croix sera notre espérance / dans notre nuit, Seigneur Jésus.

7. Un jour enfin naîtra l'aurore, / nous te verrons, Seigneur Jésus.

Dominique Ombrie 1963

2. A love much stronger than our sadness / has made us one, Lord Jesus (Christ).

3. In all our anguish, all our darkness, / we search for you, Lord Jesus (Christ).

4. And in our discords, though they wound you, / we plead with you, Lord Jesus (Christ).

5. You came among us once, a poor man, / to save us all, Lord Jesus (Christ).

6. And in our night, your Cross of sorrow / shall be our hope, Lord Jesus (Christ).

7. But when, at last, your day is dawning / we shall see you, Lord Jesus (Christ).

F. Pratt Green 1972

55

Norway
Ludwig Lindemann 19th century

1. Lord Christ when first thou cam'st to men up-on a cross— they

bound— thee, and mock'd thy sa-ving king-ship then by thorns with which— they

crowned— thee: and still our wrongs may weave thee now

new thorns to pierce that stea-dy brow, and robe of sor - row round—thee.

2. O aweful love which found no room / in life where sin denied thee, / and, doom'd to death, must bring to doom / the power which crucified thee, / till not a stone was left on stone, / and all a nation's pride o'erthrown / went down to dust beside thee!

3. New advent of the love of Christ, / shall we again refuse thee, / till in the night of hate and war / we perish as we lose thee? / From old unfaith our souls release / to seek the kingdom of thy peace / by which alone we choose thee.

4. O wounded hands of Jesus, build / in us thy new creation; / our pride is dust, our vaunt is stilled, / we wait thy revelation; / O love that triumphs over loss, / we bring our hearts before thy cross, / to finish thy salvation.

Walter Russell Bowie 1928

56

Germany
Johannes Petzold 1939

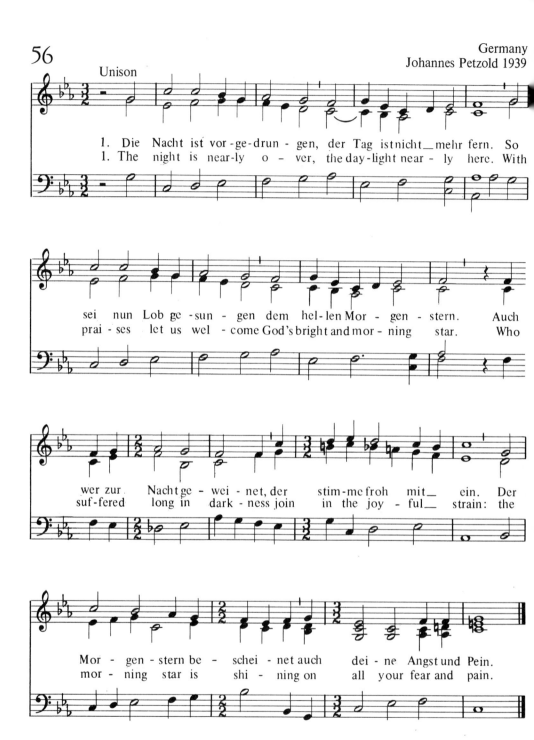

1. Die Nacht ist vor-ge-drun - gen, der Tag ist nicht mehr fern. So
1. The night is near-ly o - ver, the day-light near - ly here. With

sei nun Lob ge -sun - gen dem hel-len Mor-gen - stern. Auch
prai - ses let us wel - come God's bright and mor - ning star. Who

wer zur Nacht ge - wei - net, der stim-me froh mit_ ein. Der
suf-fered long in dark - ness join in the joy - ful_ strain: the

Mor - gen - stern be - schei - net auch dei - ne Angst und Pein.
mor - ning star is shi - ning on all your fear and pain.

114

2. Dem alle Engel dienen, wird nun ein Kind und Knecht. / Gott selber ist erschienen zur Sühne für sein Recht. / Wer schuldig ist auf Erden, verhüll nicht mehr sein Haupt. / Er soll errettet werden, wenn er dem Kinde glaubt.

3. Die Nacht ist schon im Schwinden, macht euch zum Stalle auf! / Ihr sollt das Heil dort finden, das aller Zeiten Lauf / von Anfang an verkündet, seit eure Schuld geschah. / Nun hat sich euch verbündet, den Gott selbst ausersah!

4. Noch manche Nacht wird fallen auf Menschenleid und -schuld. / Doch wandert nun mit allen der Stern der Gotteshuld. / Beglänzt von seinem Lichte, hält euch kein Dunkel mehr, / von Gottes Angesichte kam euch die Rettung her.

5. Gott will im Dunkel wohnen und hat es doch erhellt! / Als wollte er belohnen, so richtet er die Welt! / Der sich den Erdkreis baute, der lässt den Sünder nicht. / Wer hier dem Sohn vertraute, kommt dort aus dem Gericht!

Jochen Klepper 1938

2. He who was served by angels, comes as a child to serve; / for God atones in mercy the justice we deserve. / Whoever here is guilty, who knows himself defiled: / Look up! and find salvation, believing in this child.

3. How quickly night is passing – haste to the stable now! There you will find salvation; the reason why and how / God from your guilt's beginning has heard you when you cried. / Now he whom God has chosen is standing at your side.

4. As long as nights are falling on human guilt and pain, / the star of God's good pleasure will shine on travelling men. / In souls lit by its radiance the darkness cannot brood: / look up! for your salvation shines from the face of God!

5. God wants to live in darkness, so he can make it bright: / as though he would reward it he guides the world aright. / He who created all things does not forsake the lost: / Who trusts the Son as Saviour wins discharge at the last.

F. Pratt Green 1972

115

Unison

1. Ben - di - to el Rey que vie - ne en el nom-bre del Se - ñor! Al -
1. Blest be the King whose co - ming is in the name of God! For

- zad, al - zad las puer - tas del du - ro co - ra - zón! No
him let doors be o - pened, no hearts a - gainst him barred! Not

vie - ne re - ves - ti - do de su ro - pa - je real: su
robed in roy - al splen - dour, in power and pomp, comes he: but

tú - ni - ca es de sier - - vo, tal es su hu - mil - dad.
clad as are the poor - - est, such his hu - mi - li - ty!

2. Bendito el rey que viene en el nombre del Señor! / Atentos los oídos, atentos a su voz! / Pues ay del que orgulloso no quiere percibir / al Cristo prometido que viene a redimir!

3. Bendito el rey que viene en el nombre del Señor! / Que muestre a los humildes la faz del santo Dios; / a quien le han sido dadas la gloria y el poder, / que al fin de las edades los pueblos han de ver.

4. Bendito el rey que viene en el nombre del Señor! / Que ofrece a los cansados descanso y salvación. / Es manso y es humilde y en su servicio está / el yugo que nos lleva a eterna libertad.

Federico J. Pagura 1960

2. Blest be the King whose coming is in the name of God! / By those who truly listen his voice is truly heard. / Pity the proud and haughty, who have not learned to heed / the Christ who is the Promise and has our ransom paid.

3. Blest be the King whose coming is in the name of God! / He only to the humble reveals the face of God. / All power is his, all glory! All things are in his hand, / all ages and all peoples, till time itself shall end!

4. Blest be the King whose coming is in the name of God! / He offers to the burdened the rest and grace they need. / Gentle is he and humble! And light his yoke shall be, / for he would have us bear it so he can make us free!

F. Pratt Green 1973

58

Divinum Mysterium

Unison

1. Cor - de na - tus ex pa - ren - tis an - te mun - di ex-or - di - um,
1. Of the Fa-ther's heart be-got - ten ere the world from cha - os rose,

Alpha et Ome - ga cog - no - min - a - tus, ip - se fons et clau - su - ra.
he is Al - pha: from that foun - tain all that is and hath been flows:

O - mni-um quae sunt, fu - er - - - unt, quae-que post fu -
He is O - me - ga, of all_____ things yet to come the

- tu - ra sunt, Sae - cu - lo - rum sae - cu - lis._____
mys - tic close, e - ver - more and e - ver - more._____

2. O beatus ortus ille, / virgo cum puerpera / Edidit nostram salutem / foeta sancto Spiritu, / Et puer redemptor orbis / os sacratum protulit / Saeculorum saeculis.

3. Psallat altitudo caeli, / psallant omnes angeli, / Quidquid est virtutis usquam / psallat in laudem Dei, / Nulla linguarum silescat, / voce et omnis consonet / Saeculorum saeculis.

4. Ecce, quem vates vetustis / concinebant saeculis, / Quem prophetarum fideles / paginae spoponderant, / Emicat promissus olim, / cuncta collaudent cum / Saeculorum saeculis.

Prudentius, b. 348

2. By his word was all created; / he commanded and 'twas done; / earth and sky and boundless ocean, / universe of Three in One, / all that sees the moon's soft radiance, / all that breathes beneath the sun: / Evermore and evermore.

3. This is he whom seer and sybil / sang in ages long gone by; / this is he of old revealed / in the page of prophecy; / lo! he comes, the promised Saviour; / let the world his praises cry, / evermore and evermore.

4. Sing, ye heights of heaven, his praises; / angels and archangels, sing! / Wheresoe'er ye be, ye faithful, / let your joyous anthems ring, / every tongue his name confessing, / countless voices answering, / evermore and evermore.

R. F. Davis 1906

59

England
Malcolm Stewart 1969

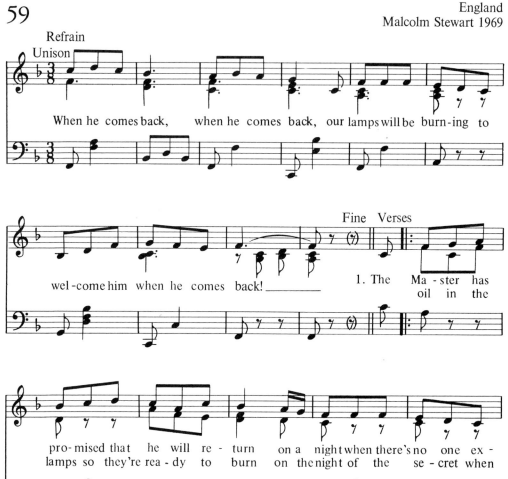

Refrain

Unison

When he comes back, when he comes back, our lamps will be burn-ing to

wel-come him when he comes back! 1. The Ma-ster has

Fine   Verses

oil in the

pro-mised that he will re - turn on a night when there's no one ex -
lamps so they're rea - dy to burn on the night of the se - cret when

- pect-ing to see him at all. Keep
those who are wait - ing he'll call.

1   **2**   D.C. al Fine

2. Look not for the Master in heaven's dark space: / by the light of our living on earth we'll discover his face. / The face of the Master is always at hand / in the face of the stranger, the poor, in the face of a man.

3. This stranger will search for his home in the night, / and then how will he find it, unless all the windows are bright? / But if we are waiting, why then, he'll come in – / and there'll be a homecoming, with dancing and singing within!

Malcolm Stewart 1969

Germany
Gottfried Neubert und Seminargruppe, Frankfurt 1964
Harm. Herbert Beuerle 1971

60

Unison

1. Kommt Gott als Mensch ___ in Dorf und Stadt, hat er nicht viel zu
    Kir - chen viel zu klein, wo die Cho - rä - le
1. God will, when he ___ comes down to earth, have lit - tle ground for
    chur - ches are too small, where hymns are sung on

la - chen. Das Chri - sten - volk ___ ist lau und matt, ver -
klin - gen. Läßt Gott sich mit ___ den Men - schen ein, kann
laugh - ter; he'll find the Christ - ians cold and slack, con -
Sun - day. When God's with man, ___ the ve - ry streets will

[continued overleaf

121

- strickt in eig - ne Sa - chen. Doch er zieht ein für
auch die Stra-ße sin - gen. Ho - san - na kommt vom
- tent with arch and raf - ter. But he is there for
shout for joy on Mon - day! Ho - san - na from the

je - der-mann, denkt nicht nur an die From-men. Er will für
Stra - ßen-rand und von den Kir-chen-bän - ken, doch er weiß,
ev' - ry man, his thought is with the low - ly, not on - ly
pa - ving stones, and from the con-gre - ga - tion! He knows our

al - le kom-men.
was wir den -ken. 2. Drum sind die und in Stras-sen.
with the ho - ly.
me - di - ta - tion. 2. That's why the on the Mon-day.

3. Kommt Gott als Mensch in Dorf und Stadt, / hat er nicht viel zu lachen: / Wir setzen ihn am Kreuze matt, / um weiter Krieg zu machen. / Auch Schweigen wird uns zum Gericht / in Kirchen und in Straßen. / Gott läßt nicht mit sich spaßen!

4. Drum sind die Kirchen viel zu klein, / wo die Choräle klingen: / Die ganze Welt muß Schauplatz sein, / wenn wir von neuem singen. / Es fängt mit dem Erschrecken an, / das wir so lieblos leben. / Der Richter hat vergeben.

5. Kommt Gott als Mensch in Dorf und Stadt, / Kann der nur wieder lachen, / der nicht mehr weiter lau und matt / das eigne Spiel will machen. / Wer Gottes Anspiel weiterspielt, / wird dies auch sehen lassen / in Kirchen und in Straßen.

Dieter Trautwein 1964

3. God will, when he comes down to earth, have little ground for laughter; / again we nail him to the cross / and go to war and slaughter. / But even silence spells our guilt / in churches and in cities. / Pray God that he has pity!

4. That's why the churches are too small / with singing congregations: / the world itself must be the stage / for workday celebrations. / It starts when people see with fright / their loveless ways of living. / God knows, we need forgiving.

5. There will, when God comes down to earth, / be only ground for laughter / with those who leave their selfish game / and join to follow after / the God who teaches us the round / from worship on the Sunday / to service on the Monday.

Fred Kaan 1972

Germany
Gerd Watkinson, 1967
Harm. C.D.

61

Solo (or semi-chorus)
Unison

1. Wer kann mir sa-gen, wo Je - sus Chri-stus ge - bo - ren ist?
1. O who can tell me where Je - sus Christ is born to - day?

All

Dort ist Chri-stus ge - bo - ren, wo Men-schen be - gin - nen,
Christ is born__ to - day,_____ where men are be - gin - ning

mensch - lich zu han - deln und sich be - sin - nen, die
to live as bro - thers, and aim at win - ning a

Welt zu ver - wan-deln. Dort __ ist Chri-stus ge - bo - ren.
new world for o - thers, Christ__ is born__ to - day.__

2. Wer kann mir sagen, wann Jesus Christus geboren ist? / Dann ist Christus geboren, wenn Menschen beginnen, / menschlich zu handeln und sich besinnen, die Welt zu verwandeln. / Dann ist Christus geboren.

3. Wer kann mir sagen, wozu Jesus Christus geboren ist? / Dazu ist Christus geboren, daß Menschen beginnen, / menschlich zu handeln und sich besinnen, die Welt zu verwandeln. / Dazu ist Christus geboren.

Kurt Rommel 1967

2. O who can tell me when Jesus Christ is born today? / Christ is born today when men are beginning / to live as brothers and aim at winning / a new world for others / Christ is born that day.

3. O who can tell me why Jesus Christ is born today? / Christ is born today that men should *begin* / to live as brothers, and aim at winning / a new world for others / Christ is born for *this*.

Emily Chisholm 1973

62

My soul doth mag-ni-fy the Lord, my spi-rit doth re-joice in God my Sa-viour, for his word de-clared to me, the choice of his hand-mai-den to be-come the mo-ther of the Christ that for the Son of God my home and hum-ble heart suf-ficed.

2. Behold, from henceforth to my name / shall generations give / their blessings, for the Lord who came / as man with man to live. / The mercy of our God is great / and great his deeds of love; / he looked upon man's low estate / and lifted him above.

3. The proud he scattered in their pride, / the rich must empty go. / The strong his strength doth set aside, / the mighty are brought low. / The humble are exalted high, / the hungry filled with food. / The God of Israel has drawn nigh, / the Lord, our God, is good.

D. T. Niles 1963

63

1. Au - jour - d'hui dans no - tre mon-de le Verbe est né
1. Lo! to - day in - to our world___ the Word is born,

pour par - ler du Pè - re aux hom-mes qu'il a tant ai - més.
to de - clare to men the Fa-ther's deep love and con - cern.

[E. v. 4]

Et le ciel nous ap - prend le grand mys - tè - - re.
Heav'n it - self tea - ches us how great the mys - te - ry:

Gloi - re à Dieu et paix sur ter - re, al - lé - lu - ia!
Glo - ry to God, and peace on earth,___ al - le - lu - ia!

[vv. 2, 3, 4 overleaf

127

2. Aujourd'hui dans nos ténèbres le Christ a lui / pour ouvrir les yeux des hommes qui vont dans la nuit. / L'univers est baigné de sa lumière: / Gloire à Dieu et paix sur terre, alléluia!

3. Aujourd'hui dans notre mort a paru la Vie / pour changer le cœur des hommes qui sont endurcis, / et l'amour est plus fort que nos misères: / Gloire à Dieu et paix sur terre, alléluia!

4. Aujourd'hui, dans notre chair est entré Jésus / pour unir en lui les hommes qui l'ont attendu. / Et Marie, à genoux, l'offre à son Père: / Gloire à Dieu et paix sur terre, alléluia!

Didier Rimaud 1958

2. Lo! today into our darkness has shone the Light, / to restore eyesight to men who are groping in night. / All his vast universe bathes in his mystery: / Glory to God, and peace on earth. Alleluia!

3. Lo! today into our death the Life breaks in, / to transform the hearts of men who are hardened by sin. / Love shall be stronger far than all our misery: / Glory to God and peace on earth. Alleluia!

4. Lo! today into our flesh the Lord descends / to unite the men who wait to be counted his friends; / offering him to his Father, Mary kneels reverently: / Glory to God and peace on earth. Alleluia!

F. Pratt Green 1972

France
Mélodie traditionelle d'Auvergne
Harm. M. E. Rose

64

Unison

1. Tout le ciel s'em-plit d'u-ne joie nou-vel - le: on en-tend la
1. All the sky is bright, fill'd with joy, a new joy. Wait-ing for the

nuit di-re la mer-veil - le. Fê-te sans pa-reil - le:
night, we will talk of won - ders. Ne-ver was a feast like this:

Le Sau-veur est né; l'en-fant Dieu nous est don - né.
Born is Je - sus Christ, born the Child-God giv'n to us!

2. Le Seigneur parait, verbe de lumière / l'univers connait la bonté du
Père. / Dieu de notre terre vient tracer la voie où chemineront nos pas.

3. Avec les bergers, avec tous les sages, / c'est le monde entier qui vers
lui s'engage / pour voir le visage de l'Amour vivant qui pour nous s'est
fait enfant.

4. Gloire à Jésus-Christ, gloire au Fils du Père! / Gloire à son Esprit dont
l'amour éclaire / l'eclatant mystère qui remplit le ciel: Gloire à l'homme-
Dieu! Noël!

Claude Rozier 1956

2. Now our Lord appears, he whose word enlightens, / all creation hears
of the Father's goodness. / He, the God of this poor earth. He has come
to show where our wand'ring steps should go.

3. Not alone they come, simple shepherds, wise men: / all the human
race wants to make him welcome, / wants to look upon the face of the
Lord of bliss, / who becomes a child for us.

4. Glory be to Christ, glory to the Father's Son, / and the Holy Ghost, he
whose love enlightens! / Dazzling is the mystery filling all the sky: / To
the Man-God 'Glory' cry!

F. Pratt Green 1972

England
Melody probably by J. F. Wade 1751
Harm. C.D.

65

1. Ad- es - te fi - de - les, lae - ti tri - um - phan - tes, ve - ni - te, ve -
1. O come, all ye faith - ful, joy - ful and tri - um - phant, O come ye, O

- ni - te in Beth - le - hem. Na - tum vi - de - te,
come— ye to Beth - le - hem; come and be - hold him,

Unison

re - gem an - ge - lo - rum: Ve - ni - te, ad - o - re - mus, ve - ni - te, a - do -
born the King of an - gels: O come, let us a - dore him, O come, let us a -

130

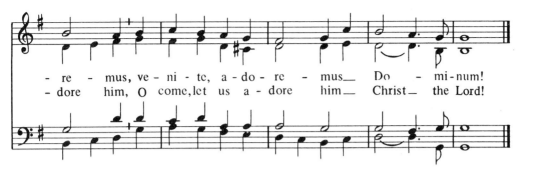

- re - mus, ve - ni - te, a - do - re - mus__ Do - mi - num!
- dore him, O come, let us a - dore him__ Christ__ the Lord!

2. Deum de Deo, Lumen de lumine, / Gestant puellae viscera; / Natum videte regem angelorum: / Venite, adoremus, venite, adoremus, / Venite, adoremus Dominum!

3. Cantet nunc 'Io!' Chorus angelorum, / Cantet nunc aula caelestium, / Gloria in excelsis Deo! / Venite, adoremus, venite adoremus, / Venite, adoremus Dominum!

4. Ergo qui natus, die hodierna, / Jesu, tibi sit gloria; / Patris aeterni, Verbum caro factum! / Venite, adoremus, venite adoremus, / Venite, adoremus Dominum!

(Anonymus)

2. God of God: Light of Light: / Lo! he abhors not the virgin's womb; / Very God, begotten, not created: / O come, let us adore him, O come, let us adore him, / O come, let us adore him, Christ the Lord!

3. Sing, choirs of angels, sing in exultation, / sing all ye citizens of heav'n above! / Glory to God in the highest! / O come, let us adore him, O come let us adore him, / O come, let us adore him, Christ the Lord!

4. Yea, Lord, we greet thee, born this happy morning, / Jesu, to thee be glory given: / Word of the Father, now in flesh appearing: / O come, let us adore him, O come let us adore him, / O come, let us adore him, Christ the Lord!

F. Oakeley 1841, 1852

Jesus Christ · His Ministry and Teaching
Jesus Christus · Dienst und Lehre
Jésus Christ · Ministère et Enseignement

66

Germany
Dieter Trautwein
Harm. Hans Rudolf Siemoneit 1964

Unison Refrain

Herr, laß uns hö-ren, was du sagst! Sprich durch die Wor-te,
Lord, let us lis-ten when you speak! Speak through the words that

die wir re-den! Hilf uns, dir ge-hor-sam sein!
we are u-sing! Help us to o-bey____ you, Lord!

Herr, laß uns hö-ren, was du ____ sagst!
Lord, let us lis-ten when you ____ speak!

Solo or semichorus

1. Ihr sollt Chri-sti Fü-ße
1. You are Christ's feet____

sein heu - te   in der Welt: geht   hin - aus und spürt die   Menschen   auf
here to -day   in the world;   go,   dis - co -ver all   the   peo - ple   who

⊕ End of final refrain

in ih - rer Not.   (4) Herr, laß uns hö-ren, was   du ____ sagst!
are most   in need.   (4) Lord, let   us lis-ten when you   speak!

2. Ihr sollt Christi Augen sein heute in der Welt: / Blickt auch hinter die Fassaden, wo das Unrecht schreit!

3. Ihr sollt Christi Hände sein heute in der Welt: / Greift nun zu und tut das Gute, wo es Menschen hilft!

4. Ihr sollt Christi Lippen sein heute in der Welt: / Redet von des Menschen Rettung, die durch ihn geschah!

Dieter Trautwein + Kurt Rommel 1964

2. You are Christ's eyes here today in the world: / look behind all our pretences when injustice shouts!

3. You are Christ's hands here today in the world: / so by grasping life do all the good you can and should!

4. You are Christ's lips here today in the world: / speak of that amazing rescue he has carried out!

F. Pratt Green 1972

67

Finland
Juhani Forsberg 1969

Unison

1. Jee - sus saa - pui Ka - per - nau - miin, ko - ti kau - pun - kiin - sa
1. Je - sus Christ has come in - to Ca - per - na - um, his ci - ty,

mai - ne kul - ki juo - rut juok - si koh - ta ym - pä riin - sä
some there are who praise him, but the o - thers shout in pro - test.

E - li - aak - si kut - sut - tiin ja jos - kus pro - fee - tak - si.
'He must be E - li - jah or a - no - ther of the pro - phets!'

Recitative

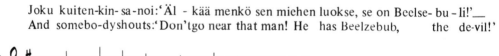

Joku kuiten - kin - sa - noi: 'Äl - kää menkö sen miehen luokse, se on Beelse - bu - li!'__
And somebo - dy shouts: 'Don't go near that man! He has Beelzebub, the de - vil!'

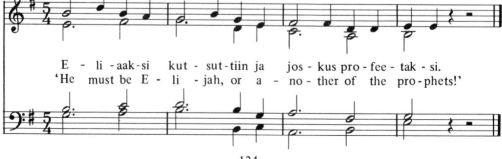

E - li - aak - si kut - sut - tiin ja jos - kus pro - fee - tak - si.
'He must be E - li - jah, or a - no - ther of the pro - phets!'

134

2. Tungoksessa valtavassa Jeesus puhuu sanaa / neljä miestä paarein
päällä halvattua kantaa / ovesta ei sisään pääse, katto täytyy purkaa / joku
sanoi: 'kuka nyt tolla tavalla rupee saarnaa häiritsemään?' / ovesta ei
sisään pääse, katto täytyy purkaa

3. Paarit maahan laskettiin ja Jeesus sairaan näki / lausui sanan, kohta
sitä ihmetteli väki: / 'poikani, sun syntisi on pyyhitty pois kaikki' / joku
sanoi: 'onko nyt laitaa puhua synnistä kun toinen on kuolemansairas?' / ja
moni mietti: (lausuen) 'kuinka hän voi antaa syntejä anteeksi? hän pilkkaa
Jumalaa!' / poikani, sun syntisi on pyyhitty pois kaikki

4. Arvoituksen pulmallisen Jeesus heille antaa: / kumpi näistä helpompaa
nyt oikein olla mahtaa: / synnit antaa anteeksi vai halvattua auttaa /
Jeesus sanoi: 'koska Ihmisen Pojalla on valta anteeksi antaa, niin minä
sanon: / nouse, ota vuoteesi ja täältä kotiin lähde'

5. Polvin hieman horjuvin hän matkaan lähti sieltä / mennessänsä
kiitosvirsi kuulu kotitieltä: / 'halleluja halleluja kiitos Jumalalle!' / silloin
kaikki sanoivat: 'tämän kaltaista emme ole ikinä nähneet / halleluja
halleluja kiitos Jumalalle!'

Juhani Forsberg 1969

2. In the overcrowded house the Lord speaks to the people. / Look,
they're bringing in the paralytic on a stretcher. / 'Crowds are blocking up
the door. You'll have to break the roofing.' / And somebody shouts: 'You
can't disturb a sermon like this!' / 'Crowds are blocking up the door,
you'll have to break the roofing!'

3. As he lies before his feet, the Lord looks at the sufferer, / speaks a
powerful word to him, and many are offended: / 'Son, your past is
washed away, your sins are all forgotten!' And someone calls out,
'Talking of his sins, and the man so ill!' / And many are thinking: 'How
can he forgive sins? This is blasphemy.' / 'Son, your sin is washed away.
Your sins are all forgiven!'

4. Jesus puts a question now, and asks them for the answer: / 'Tell me,
anybody, which is easier to manage, / Sinful man to pardon, or to cure
the paralytic?' / And Jesus says to them: 'Since the Son of Man has
power to forgive sins, / I say: "stand up straight, take up your bed, and
walk home through the city!"

5. And the man stands up and walks, although his knees are shaking. /
All can see that he can walk. They listen to his praises. / 'Alleluia!
Alleluia! Thanks to God Almighty!' / And they all are amazed: 'We have
never seen anything like it!' / 'Alleluia! Alleluia! Thanks to God
Almighty!'

Emily Chisholm 1972

68 Organic Introduction

Wales
William Llewellyn 1969

★Note: Each bar, whether 2/4 or 3/4, is to have the same duration.

136

Blest are the meek: for they shall in-he-rit the earth.

Show us your ways, O Lord, teach us your paths. ___ Blest are

they that hun-ger and thirst af-ter right-eous-ness: for they shall

___ be filled. Blest are the mer-ci-ful: for

137

[continued overleaf

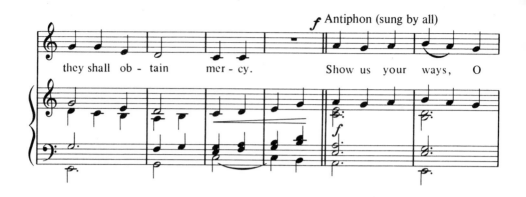

they shall ob-tain mer-cy. Show us your ways, O

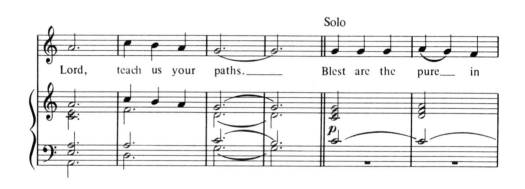

Lord, teach us your paths._____ Blest are the pure__ in

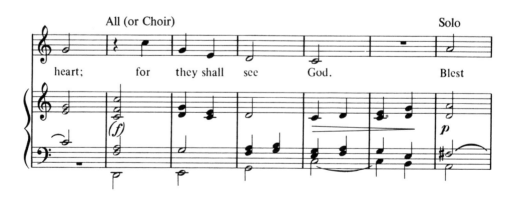

heart; for they shall see God. Blest

are the peace-ma-kers; for they shall be called God's sons.

Solo

Blest are they which are per-se-cu-ted for right-eous-ness'

All (or Choir)

sake: the king-dom of heaven is theirs.

Antiphon (sung by all)

Show us your ways, O Lord, teach us your paths.

Scripture, St. Matthew 5, 3 - 10 / Psalm 25, 4

69

Sweden
Roland Forsberg 1970

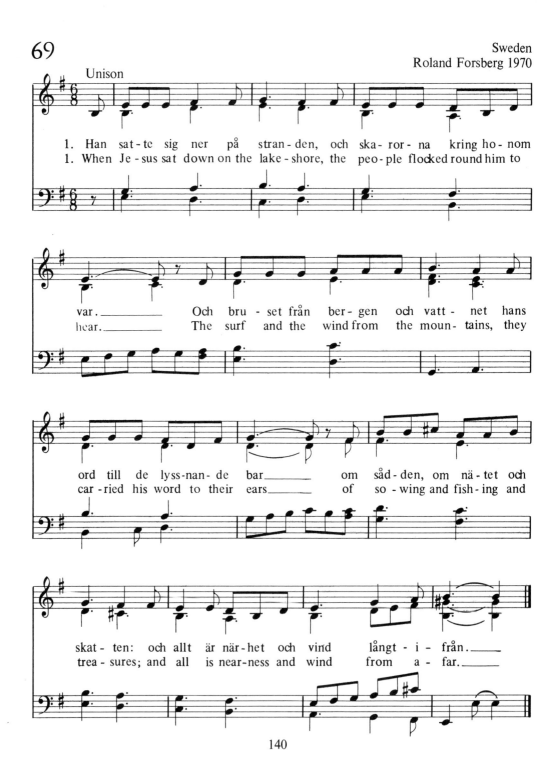

Unison

1. Han sat-te sig ner på stran-den, och ska-ror-na kring ho-nom
1. When Je-sus sat down on the lake-shore, the peo-ple flocked round him to

var._____ Och bru-set från ber-gen och vatt-net hans
hear._____ The surf and the wind from the moun-tains, they

ord till de lyss-nan-de bar_____ om såd-den, om nä-tet och
car-ried his word to their ears_____ of so-wing and fish-ing and

skat-ten: och allt är när-het och vind långt-i-från._____
trea-sures; and all is near-ness and wind from a-far._____

2. Han satte sig ner vid brunnen. / En synderska hos honom stod, en utstött: / ur staden fördriven av rädslan för mänskornas dom. / Han gav henne åter till livet; / och allt är närhet och väg låntifrån.

3. Han satte sig ner i öknen / den sjuke till honom man bar. / Och borta var plågan och döden. / 'Gå hem till de dina i dag!' / De hungriga räckte han bröden: / och alet är närhet och makt långtifrån.

4. Han sitter på högra sidan / om Fadern. Hos alla han är. / På gatan han går och vid bordet / han tjänande böjer sig ner. / Hans röst vi förnimmer ur Ordet: / och allt är närhet. Vår värld är hans värld.

Anders Frostenson 1970

2. When Jesus sat down at the wellside, / a woman came out of the town, / rejected by public opinion / because of her doubtful renown; / but Jesus restored her to living: / and all is nearness and streams from afar.

3. When Jesus sat down in the desert, / they brought to him those who were ill. / He healed their despair and diseases: / 'Arise and go home: you are well!' / And then he broke bread with the hungry: / and all is nearness and strength from afar.

4. And now he is with us for ever: / he sits at the Father's right hand: / he serves us at table, we meet him / in city streets and on the land. / His word is our hope and our challenge: / and all is nearness, for his is the world!

Fred Kaan 1973

70

Chorus

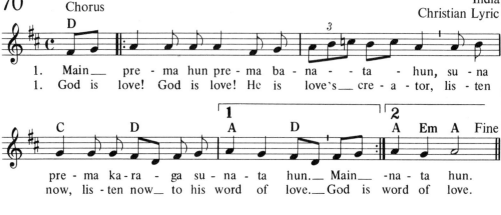

1. Main__ pre - ma hun pre - ma ba - na - - ta - hun, su - na
1. God is love! God is love! He is love's__ cre - a - tor, lis - ten

pre - ma ka - ra - ga su - na - ta hun.__ Main__ -na - ta hun.
now, lis - ten now__ to his word of love.__God is word of love.

Verses

Is - a ja - ga ke na - hin ji - s(a) men__ tu - m(a) ho
You are in this world of mine, but you are not of the world.

I - sa men du - kha hai - du - kh(a) pa - ta hun.__
All its sor - row I bear,__ and you bear it with me.

2. Sab(a) dush(a) mano ko tuma piyar(a) karo / Main prem(a) se kashta uthata hun.

3. Main prema ki khushobu sekhush(a) hun / aura prema ka baga lagata hun.

4. Main yesa na hobezarana ho / main teredil(a) men ata hun.

Bantam Ram Banda (Hindustani)

2. You must love all those who are enemies to you: / all your burdens I bear, all your stress and sorrow.

3. I shall sow seeds of love in the garden of love, / and the scent of their flowers will always delight me.

4. Do not weep, do not fear, let your courage burn bright; / for this is my promise: I am with you always.

Erik Routley 1972

71

Sri Lanka
Popular melody
Harm. C.D.

1. Son of the Fa - ther,— Je - sus, Lord and slave, born a - mong the cat - tle in the squa - lor of a cave, one with God, you made your-self one with man, shun-ning wealth; Lord, we wor - ship you with heart and mind.

[vv. 2, 3, 4, 5 overleaf

2. Son of the Father, Jesus, worker's friend, / you whom Joseph taught the skills of working with your hands, / man, at home in builder's yard, / one with man, toiling hard; / Lord, we worship you with hand and mind.

3. Son of the Father, author of our faith, / choosing men to follow you from every walk of life, / who with them, in boats, on shore, / troubles shared, burdens bore; / Lord, we worship you with hand and mind.

4. Seed of the Father, from life's furrow born, / teaching men in parables from agriculture drawn, / Jesus, lover of the soil, / man of earth, son of toil; / Lord, we worship you with hand and mind.

5. Father and Spirit, Jesus, Lord and Man, / bless us in the work you have appointed to be done. / Lift our spirits, guide our wills, / steer our hands, use our skills; / Lord, we worship you with hand and mind.

Fred Kaan 1972

Sweden
Carl Nielsen 1917

1. Där - för att Or - det bland oss bor blir värl-den ald - rig stum. En
1. How can cre- a -tion's voice be still, when with us dwells the Word? A

lov - sång lyfts. Vi väcks till tro i vår för-tviv - lans stund.
song of praise is raised from earth; faith ri - ses like a bird.

2. I stoft, i gräsens bräcklighet, / hos den som hjälplös böjs / bor Gud i samma majestät / som in sin himmels höjd.

3. Den gode herdens röst blir hörd / ur rop, som tystas ner. / Bland orm och varg Guds hjord blir förd / och intet ont den sker.

4. Den sten som framför graven ställts / är Paradisets port / och hjärtan tänds i pingstens eld / och språken smälts ihop.

5. Därför att ordet bland oss bor / har världen ljus och liv. / Ge oss, o Gud, en lyhörd tro / en öppen, vaksam blick.

Anders Frostenson 1962

2. God dwells as much in grass and dust, / in human souls weighed down, / as in the realm of majesty, / the heavens and their span.

3. The shepherd's voice is heard to call / through voices that are stilled. / The flock is led in danger's face / but shall not come to ill.

4. The stone is rolled away; the tomb / becomes the gate to life. / The earth is warmed by tongues of fire / that speak, and none is deaf.

5. The Word is with us, and the world / is full of light and life. / Lord, give us faithfulness and faith, / alert and seeing eyes.

Fred Kaan 1973

145

Germany
Gerhard Kloft 1965

Refrain
Unison

Wir sind nicht ir-gend-wer___ und nicht nur un-ge-fähr,___
We're not just a-ny-one;___ we're not just no-bo-dies;___

son-dern ganz Got-tes Kin-der, Got-tes Kin-der.
we're com-plete-ly God's chil-dren, God's___ chil-dren.

1. Ihr sollt nicht irgendwer, sondern Gottes Kinder sein / Kinder Gottes, erkannt am Gehorsam. / Ihr sollt nicht irgendwie wieder die Dummen sein, / haltlos von Selbstsucht getrieben.

2. Er ist nicht irgendwer! Der euch beruft, ist selbst heilig. / Ihr sollt nicht irgendwie, sondern wie Christus sein. / Heilig heißt: Gott ganz zu eigen!

3. Er ist nicht irgendwer. Der Vater, der Taten richtet, / zieht euch nicht andern vor. / Ihr sollt nicht irgendwie, sondern mit Sorgfalt die Tage verbringen.

4. Ihr seid nicht irgendwer, sondern befreiten Sklaven gleich, / los von der Jagd nach dem Leben. / Er war nicht irgendwer, Christus vergab sein Leben, / daß ihr frei sein und leben könnt.

Dieter Trautwein, 1965, based on I Peter 1, 4-19

(Die Verse werden über improvisierter Musik gesprochen, der Refrain zwischen den Strophen gesungen)

1. You're not just anyone, you're God's own children, / yes, children of God, proved so by obedience. / You must not be a stupid person, / always driven anyhow by selfishness.

2. He's not just anyone! He who calls you is himself holy. / You mustn't live just anyhow, but as Christ lived. / Being holy is making God one's own.

3. He's not just anyone: the Father in his actions does not prefer you to others. / You mustn't live just anyhow, but spend the days that are yours with due care.

4. You're not just anyone, but all the same are slaves set free, free from the hue and cry of life. / He wasn't just anyone, for Christ gave up his life so that you might be free and might live.

F. Pratt Green 1972

(Verses spoken above improvised music: the refrain is sung and can be repeated)

74

Netherlands
T. de M. Oyens 1959

1. Zo - lang er Men - sen zijn op aar - de, zo -
1. As long as peo - ple walk this pla - net, as

- lang de aar - de vruch-ten geeft, zo - lang zijt Gij ons al - ler
long as earth has fruit to give, so long are you our lov-ing

wij dan - ken_____ voor al wat leeft.
Va - der, wij dan - ken U___ voor al wat leeft. _____
Fa - ther, we thank you for___ all things that live. _____
wij dan - ken U voor al wat leeft.

wij dan - ken U__ voor al wat leeft.

147

[vv. 2, 3, 4, 5 overleaf

2. Zolang de mensen woorden spreken, / zolang wij voor elkaar bestaan, / zolang zult Gij ons niet ontbreken, / wij danken U in Jezus' naam.

3. Gij voedt de vogels in de bomen, / Gij kleedt de bloemen op het veld, / O Heer Gij zijt ons onderkomen / en al mijn dagen zijn geteld.

4. Gij zijt ons licht, ons eeuwig leven, / Gij redt de wereld van den dood, / Gij hebt uw Zoon aan ons gegeven, / Zijn lichaam is het levend brood.

5. Daarom moet alles U aanbidden, / uw liefde heeft het voortgebracht, / Vader, Gijzelf zijt in ons midden, / O Heer, wij zijn van uw geslacht.

Huub Oosterhuis 1965

2. As long as human words are spoken, / as long as people love and share, / then we shall never be forsaken, / we give you thanks in Jesus' name.

3. You feed the birds that flit through branches, / you clothe the flowers in wondrous ways, / O Lord, you are my home, my refuge, / and you have numbered all my days.

4. You are our light, our life eternal, / you draw the world away from death, / you sent your only son to save us, / his body is our living bread.

5. And that is why mankind should love you, / your love has fathered everything, / O Father living here among us, / O God, we are the song you sing!

Redmond McGoldrick

[*English text differs from Melody Edition*]

75

India
J. B. Fernandes, S. J. 1964

Refrain

This is my com - mand - ment: love one

an - oth - er as I have loved you.

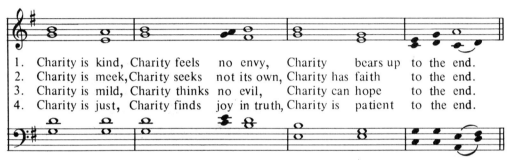

1. Charity is kind, Charity feels no envy, Charity bears up to the end.
2. Charity is meek, Charity seeks not its own, Charity has faith to the end.
3. Charity is mild, Charity thinks no evil, Charity can hope to the end.
4. Charity is just, Charity finds joy in truth, Charity is patient to the end.

T.: Scripture – I Cor. 13 and St. John 15

Composed for the occasion of Pope Paul VI's visit to India, December 1964, in connection with the Eucharistic Congress held in Bombay.

76

Brazil
José Alves 1970

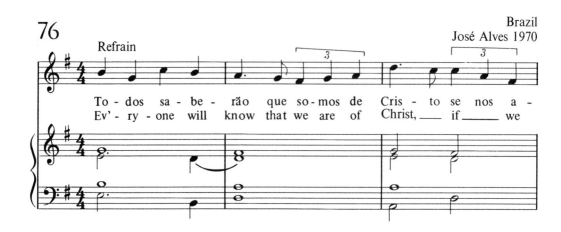

Refrain

To - dos sa - be - rão que so - mos de Cris - to se nos a -
Ev' - ry - one will know that we are of Christ, __ if __ we

Fine

- mar - mos, se nos a - mar - mos uns aos ou - tros.
love, __ if __ we love __ one an - oth - er.

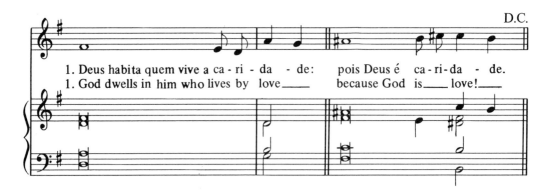

D.C.

1. Deus habita quem vive a ca - ri - da - de: pois Deus é ca - ri - da - de.
1. God dwells in him who lives by love __ because God is __ love! __

150

2. O pai nos amou com tanto amor / que para nossa vida enviou seu Filho amado.

3. Esta é a maravilha do amor / Foi Deus que nos amou por primeiro.

4. As trevas que sofremos passarão, / e brilhará para todos nós a verdadeira luz.

Jo. 13.35: I Jo. 3.3-4.7

2. The Father loved us with so great a love / that for our life he sent his beloved Son.

3. This is the marvel of his love / that it was God who loved us first.

4. The shadows which we suffered have passed / and the true Light shall shine for us all.

arranged by Helena Scott 1973

77

Brazil
José Weber 1970

Refrain

Pro - va de a - mor ma - ior não há
Great - er love has no _____ man than this:

Fine

que dó - ar a vi - da pe - lo ir - mão.
that he give his life _____ for his friends.

Solo

1. Now I

Solo

1. Eis que eu vos dou o meu nô - vo man-da - men-to: A -
give _____ you my new com - mand - - - ment: _____ [—]

152

- mai vos uns aos ou-tros co - mo eu vos ten - ho_a-ma - do.
Love__ one an - oth- er as__ I my-self have loved you.

2. Vós sereis os meus amigos, se seguirdes meu preceito: / Amaivos.

3. Como o pai sempre me ama assim também eu vos amei: / Amai-vos . . .

4. Permanecei em meu amor e segui meu mandamento. / Amai-vos . . .

5. E chegando a minha Páscoa vos amei até o fim: / Amai-vos . . .

6. Nisto todos saberao que vós sois os meus discípulos: / Amai-vos . . .

(Scripture)

2. You will be my friends if you follow my precept: /Love one another . . .

3. As the Father loves me always, so also have I loved you: /Love one another . . .

4. Be constant in my love and follow my commandment. /Love one another . . .

5. And approaching my Passover I have loved you to the end. /Love one another . . .

6. By this shall men know that you are my disciples. /Love one another . . .

arr. by Helena Scott 1973

Jesus Christ · Jesus Christus · Jésus Christ
His Atonement, Resurrection and Reign
Sühne, Auferstehung und Herrschaft
Expiation, Resurrection et Règne

78

France
J. Gelineau 1965

Semi-chorus (men)
Unison

1. Par la Croix qui fit mou-rir le fils du Pè - re, sar -
2. Par le Sang dont fut mar-qué le bois des por - tes, pour
1. By the Cross which did to death our on - ly Sa - viour, this
2. By the Blood with which we marked the wood-en lin - tels, for

All
a 4 f

- ment bé - ni où la grappe est ven-dan-gée, Jé - sus Christ, nous
nous gar - der dans la nuit où Dieu pas - sait, Je - sus Christ, we
bles - sed vine from which grapes are ga - thered in,
our pro - tec - tion the night when God passed by,

Unis. p
Semi-chorus (women or boys)

te bé - nis - sons. Par la Croix qui met le feu sur no - tre
Par le Sang qui nous sau - va dans notre ex -
thank and bless you. By the Cross which casts down fire up -on our
By the Blood which in our Ex - o - dus once

ter - re, buis-son ar - dent où l'a - mour est ré - vé - lé, Jé - sus
- o - de, lors-que les eaux sur l'en - fer se re - fer-maient, Jé - sus
pla - net, this bur -ning bush in which love is plain-ly shown, Je - sus
saved us, when hell was sealed up by God's en - gulf-ing sea, Je - sus

Semi-chorus (Soprano and/or Tenor)

Unis. *p*

Christ, nous te glo - ri - fions. Par la Croix qui fut plan -
                                  Par le Sang qui rend la
Christ, we glo - ri - fy you. By the Cross on Calv'ry's
                              By the Blood which kills the

- tée sur le Cal - vai - re, ra-meau vi - vant qui gué - rit de tout pé -
vie aux sè - ves mor - tes, en dé - trui-sant le ve - nin du fruit mau -
hill se-cure - ly plan - ted, this liv - ing branch which can heal our ev' - ry
poi - son in bad fruit-age, and gives new life to the dead sap in the

a 4 *f*

- ché, Dieu vain - queur, ton é - gli - se t'ac - cla - me.
- vais,
sin, Con - qu'ring God, we your peo - ple pro - claim_____ you!
tree,

155   [vv. 3, 4, 5 overleaf

3. Par la mort du premier-Né sur la colline / portant le bois et la flamme du bûcher, / Jésus-Christ, nous te bénissons. / Par la mort du Bon Pasteur dans les épines, / Agneau pascal dont le cœur est transpercé, / Jésus-Christ, nous te glorifions. / Par la mort du Bien-Aimé, hors de sa vigne, / pour qu'il changeât l'homicide en héritier, / Dieu vainqueur, ton Eglise t'acclame.

4. Par le Bois qui a chanté le chant des noces / du Dieu vivant épousant l'humanité, / Jésus Christ, nous te bénissons. / Par le Bois qui fait lever en pleine force / le Fils de l'Homme attirant le monde entier, / Jésus Christ, nous te glorifions. / Par le Bois où s'accomplit le Sacerdoce / du seul Grand Prêtre immolé pour le péché, / Dieu vainqueur, ton Eglise t'acclame.

5. Arbre saint qui touche au ciel depuis la terre / pour que le Dieu de Jacob soit exalté, / Jésus-Christ, nous te bénissons. / Grand Vaisseau qui nous arrache à la Colère / en nous sauvant du Déluge avec Noé, / Jésus Christ, nous te glorifions. / Tendre Bois qui adoucit les eaux amères / et fait jaillir la fontaine du Rocher, / Dieu vainqueur, ton Eglise t'acclame.

Didier Rimaud

3. By the Death on Calvary's hill of him the First-born / who bears the wood and the flame for his own pyre: / Jesus Christ, we thank and bless you! / By the Death, amid the thorns, of God's own Shepherd, / the Pascal Lamb who was pierced by our despair: / Christ Jesus, we glorify you! / By the Death of God's Beloved outside his vineyard, / that he might change us from murderer into heir: / Conquering God, we your Church proclaim you!

4. By the Wood which sings a song of nuptial gladness, / of God who takes for bride our human race: / Jesus Christ, we thank and bless you! / By the Wood which raises up in his full vigour / the Son of Man who draws all men by his grace: / Jesus Christ, we glorify you! / By the Wood where he perfects his royal Priesthood / in one High Priest who for sin is sacrifice: / Conquering God, we your Church proclaim you!

5. Holy Tree which reaches up from earth to heaven / that all the world may exult in Jacob's God: / Jesus Christ, we thank and bless you! / Mighty Ship which snatches us from God's deep anger, / saves us, with Noah, from drowning in the Flood: / Jesus Christ, we glorify you! / Tender Wood which gives to brackish water sweetness, / and from the Rock shall strike fountains for our good: / Conquering God, we your Church proclaim you!

F. Pratt Green 1972

U.S.A.
Melody from *Southern Harmony* 1835
Harm. C.D.

1. What won-drous love is this, O my soul, O my soul, what won-drous love is this, O my soul! What won-drous love is this that caused the Lord __ of bliss to lay a - side his crown for my soul, for my soul, to lay a - side his crown for my soul!

2. To God and to the Lamb I will sing, I will sing, / to God and to the Lamb I will sing; / to God and to the Lamb who is the great I AM, / while millions join the theme, I will sing, I will sing, / while millions join the theme, I will sing.

3. And when from death I'm free I'll sing on, I'll sing on, / and when from death I'm free, I'll sing on. / And when from death I'm free I'll sing and joyful be. / And through eternity I'll sing on, I'll sing on, / and through eternity I'll sing on.

American folk hymn

England
John Ireland 1919

Love unknown
a 4

1. My song is love un - known, __ my Sa-viour's love to me, love
2. He came from his blest throne, __ sal - va - tion to be - stow; but

to the love - less shown, that they might love - ly be. _____ O
men made strange, and none the longed-for Christ would know. _____ But

who am I, that for my sake __ my Lord should take frail flesh and die?
oh, my friend, my friend in-deed __ who at my need his life did spend!

3. Sometimes they strew his way and his sweet praises sing; / resounding all the day hosannas to their King. / Then 'Crucify!' is all their breath, / and for his death they thirst and cry.

4. Why, what hath my Lord done? What makes this rage and spite? / He made the lame to run, he gave the blind their sight. / Sweet injuries! Yet they at these / themselves displease, and 'gainst him rise.

5. They rise, and needs will have my dear Lord made away; / a murderer they save, the Prince of Life they slay. / Yet cheerful he to suffering goes, / that he his foes from thence might free.

6. Here might I stay and sing. No story so divine; / never was love, dear King, never was grief like thine! / This is my friend in whose sweet praise / I all my days could gladly spend.

S. Crossman 1664

81

Sweden
Verner Ahlberg 1933

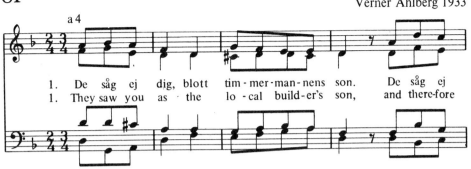

1. De såg ej dig, blott tim - mer - man - nens son. De såg ej
1. They saw you as the lo - cal build - er's son, and there - fore

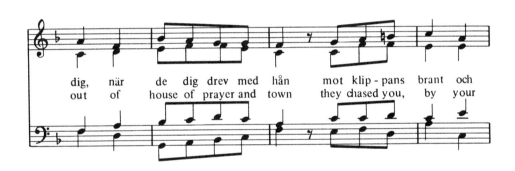

dig, när de dig drev med hån mot klip - pans brant och
out of house of prayer and town they chased you, by your

ut i en - sam natt. En falsk pro - fet de såg och en be - satt.
pro - phe - cy en - raged, in - to the dark - ness, to the moun - tain edge.

159

[vv. 2, 3, 4 overleaf

2. De såg ej dig, du världens enda hopp, / när de drev spjut och spikar i din kropp. / Guds kärlek såg de ej, en utstött blott. / De såg ej dig som sonar allas brott.

3. De såg ej dig, din hand kring smärtan krökt, / den hand som världen byggt och syndarn sökt. / De såg ej dig, som under mörknad sol / lät korset blie en evig nådastol.

4. En gång vi alla ser den nåd du gav, / som floden sedd från källan till sitt hav. / Omkring din tron förbundets båge står / och allas sår har läkts i dina sår.

Anders Frostenson 1962

2. They did not see in you the nation's hope, / or see you take and drink the bitter cup. / They did not recognize the love divine / in you, who bore away our guilt and sin.

3. They did not see your hand in anguish curled, / your hand that heals, the hand that made the world. / They failed to see, when darkness came at noon, / that on your cross your saving work was done.

4. The time will come when every man shall see / your grace is like a stream that fills the sea. / You give us of your covenant the sign, / and in your wounds you heal all human pain.

Fred Kaan 1973

82a

Germany
Hans Leo Haßler 1601, 1613
Harm. C.D.

Herzlich thut mich Verlangen

Unison

1. O Haupt voll Blut und Wun-den, voll Schmerz und vol - ler Hohn, o
1. O sac - red Head, sore wounded, with grief and shame weighed down; how

Haupt, zum Spott ge - bun-den mit ei - ner Dor - nen - kron, o
scorn - ful - ly sur - round-ed with thorns thy on - ly crown; how

Haupt, sonst schön ge - krö - net mit höch-ster Ehr und Zier,
art thou pale with an - guish, with sore a - buse and scorn;

jetzt a - ber frech ver-höh - net: Ge - grü - ßet seist du mir.
how does that vis - age lan - guish which once was bright as morn.

[vv. 2, 3 overleaf

161

2. Was du, Herr, hast erduldet, / ist alles meine Last; / ich, ich hab es verschuldet, / was du getragen hast. / Schau her, hier steh ich Armer, / der Zorn verdienet hat; / gib mir, o mein Erbarmer, / den Anblick deiner Gnad.

3. Ich danke dir von Herzen, / o Jesu, liebster Freund, / für deines Todes Schmerzen, / da du's so gut gemeint. / Ach gib, daß ich mich halte, / zu dir und deiner Treu / und, wenn ich einst erkalte, / in dir mein Ende sei.

Paul Gerhardt 1656

2. Thy grief and bitter passion / were all for sinners' gain; / mine, mine was the transgression, / but thine the deadly pain. / Lo, here I fall, my Saviour, / 'tis I deserve thy place; / Look on me with thy favour, / vouchsafe to me thy grace.

3. What language shall I borrow / to thank thee, dearest friend, / for this, thy dying sorrow, / thy pity without end? / O make me thine for ever, / and, should I fainting be, / Lord, let me never, never / outlive my love to thee.

J. W. Alexander 1861

Germany
Melody by H. L. Haßler 1564—1612
Harm. J. S. Bach

1. O Haupt voll Blut und Wun - den, voll Schmerz und vol - ler Hohn, o
1. O sac - red Head, sore wound - ed, with grief and shame weighed down; how

Haupt, zum Spott ge - bun - den mit ei - ner Dor-nen-kron, o
scorn - ful - ly sur - round - ed with thorns thy on - ly crown; how

Haupt, sonst schön ge - krö - net mit höch-ster Ehr und Zier, jetzt
art thou pale with an - guish, with sore a - buse and scorn; how

a - ber frech ver - höh - net: Ge - grü - ßet seist du mir.
does that vis - age lan - guish which once was bright as morn.

[vv. 2, 3 overleaf

163

2. Was du, Herr, hast erduldet, / ist alles meine Last; / ich, ich hab es verschuldet, / was du getragen hast. / Schau her, hier steh ich Armer, / der Zorn verdienet hat; / gib mir, o mein Erbarmer, / den Anblick deiner Gnad.

3. Ich danke dir von Herzen, / o Jesu, liebster Freund, / für deines Todes Schmerzen, / da du's so gut gemeint. / Ach gib, daß ich mich halte, / zu dir und deiner Treu / und, wenn ich einst erkalte, / in dir mein Ende sei.

Paul Gerhardt 1656

2. Thy grief and bitter passion / were all for sinners' gain; / mine, mine was the transgression, / but thine the deadly pain. / Lo, here I fall, my Saviour, / 'tis I deserve thy place; / Look on me with thy favour, / vouchsafe to me thy grace.

3. What language shall I borrow / to thank thee, dearest friend, / for this, thy dying sorrow, / thy pity without end? / O make me thine for ever, / and, should I fainting be, / Lord, let me never, never / outlive my love to thee.

J. W. Alexander 1861

83

Rockingham

1. When I____ sur - vey the won - drous Cross on which the Prince of glo - ry died,___ my rich - est gain I count__ but loss and pour__ con - tempt__ on all____ my pride.

2. Forbid it, Lord, that I should boast / save in the death of Christ my God; / all the vain things I covet most / I sacrifice them to his blood.

3. See from his head, his hands, his feet / sorrow and love flow mingled down; / did e'er such love and sorrow meet, / or thorns compose so rich a crown?

4. His dying crimson like a robe / spreads o'er his body on the tree, / then am I dead to all the globe / and all the globe is dead to me.

5. Were the whole realm of nature mine / it were a present far too small, / love so amazing, so divine, / demands my soul, my life, my all.

Isaac Watts 1674-1748

165

84

1. Ge- lobt sei Gott im höch - sten Thron samt sei - nem ein - ge - bor-nen
1. Good Christ - ian men, re - joice_ and sing! Now is the tri - umph of our_

Sohn, der für uns hat_ ge - nug ge - tan. Hal - le - lu -
King! To all the world_ glad news we_ bring: Al - le - lu -

- ja,_ Hal - le - lu - ja, _ Hal - le - lu - ja.
- ia,_ al - le - lu - ia, _ al - le - lu - ia!

2. Er ist erstanden von dem Tod, / hat überwunden alle Not; / kommt, seht, wo er gelegen hat. / Halleluja, halleluja, halleluja.

3. Nun bitten wir dich, Jesu Christ, / weil du vom Tod erstanden bist, / verleihe, was uns selig ist. / Halleluja, halleluja, halleluja.

4. Damit von Sünden wir befreit / dem Namen dein gebenedeit, / frei mögen singen allezeit: / Halleluja, halleluja, halleluja.

Michael Weisse gest. 1534

2. The Lord of life is risen for aye; / bring flowers of song to strew his way; / let all mankind rejoice and say: / Alleluia, alleluia, alleluia!

3. Praise we in songs of victory / that love, that life which cannot die, / and sing with hearts uplifted high: / Alleluia, alleluia, alleluia!

4. Thy name we bless, O risen Lord, / and sing today with one accord, / the life laid down, the life restored: / Alleluia, alleluia, alleluia!

C.A. Alington 1931

U.S.A.
Negro Spiritual
Edited by John W. Work, 1940

85

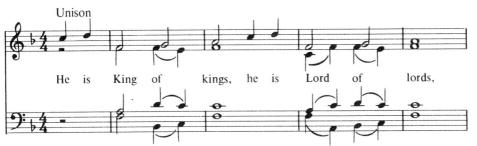

Unison

He is King of kings, he is Lord of lords,

a 4   Fine

Je - sus Christ the first and last,___ no man works like him.

Solo   Chorus
                                         a 4   Solo

1. He built his throne up in the air,___ no man works like him, and
2. He pitched his tents on Ca-naan's ground,

Chorus
a 4   D.C.

called his saints from ev' - ry - where,_ no man works like him.
broke the Ro - man king-dom down,_

86 **Kh'nga**

1. No - tre Dieu Sau - veur est Jé - sus Sei - gneur; par -
2. A Jé - ru - sa - lem c'est un jour de joie; tout
1. Our Je - sus is Sa - viour,__ Lord and friend; he
2. The ci - ty re - joi - ces, the child - ren sing: 'A

- tout il nous suit, no - tre vie, c'est lui.
le peu - ple crie 'voi - ci no - tre Roi!'
searched all our life from__ end to end.
day____ of joy: be - hold our King!'

Refrain

A Jé - sus vint . i - ci bas et ver - sa son sang au Gol -
B Chan - tons Al - lé - lu - ia, Christ est res - sus - ci - té, Al -
A And he came down to earth__ to shed his blood__ on
B Sing__ al - le - lu - ia,____ for Christ the Lord__ is

- go - tha pour nous don - ner____ sa vie.
- lé - lu - ia! pour nous don - ner____ sa vie.
Cal - va - ry, all to give life____ to men.
ri - - sen, all to give life____ to men.

3. Dans la Chambre Haute, la Table est dressée; / le pain et le vin y sont partagés. (Refrain A)

4. En lavant les pieds comme un serviteur, / il annonce aux siens son abaissement. (Refrain A)

5. Tous sont avec lui à Gethsemané; / mais devant Pilate seul il s'est trouvé. (Refrain A)

6. Pilate a jugé: il est innocent; / son peuple a crié: ôte et crucifie. (Refrain A)

7. Avant le sabbat tout est terminé; / et dans son tombeau Christ est enfermé. (Refrain A)

8. Où sont les disciples? où sont ses amis? / Le Seigneur est mort, tout est donc fini? / Pause (sans Refrain)

9. Au troisième jour la nouvelle court: / tout n'est pas fini: Jésus est vivant. / (Refrain B, bis)

10. Il est tout amour, il mourut pour nous; / il vainquit la mort, il nous rend vainqueurs. / (Refrain B)

Abel Nkuinji 1965

3. The Table is set in an upper room; / the bread and the wine foretell his doom. (Refrain A)

4. In form of a servant he washes their feet, / and says 'thus humbly each other greet.' (Refrain A)

5. They all go with him to Gethsemane, / but in Pilate's courts there is none but he. (Refrain A)

6. 'Not guilty', says Pilate, and washes his hands. / 'Away with him now!' the crowd demands. (Refrain A)

7. Before evening falls, it all is done; / the tomb receives our Holy One. (Refrain A)

8. Where are the disciples? where now are his friends? / The Lord is dead: and here all hope ends . . . Pause (no Refrain)

9. Two nights and a day, and the news is abroad: / not end but beginning! alive is the Lord! (Refrain B - twice)

10. So praise we God's love for what Jesus has done. / Now death is defeated, and victory won. / (Refrain B)

Erik Routley 1972

87

Tanzania
Joas Kijugo 1964

Solo

(1) 1. Bwa - na Ye - su ka - fu - fu - ka, a - me - to - ka ka - bu -
1. Christ is ri - sen, death is van - quished, he has left the tomb's dark

All

Hal - le -
Al - le -

Fine

- ri - ni.
pri - son.

(2) Na ma -
At the

- lu - ia, Hal - le - lu - ia, a - me - to - ka ka - bu -
- lu - ia, Al - le - lu - ia, he has left the tomb's dark

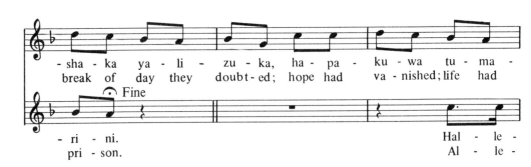

- sha - ka ya - li - zu - ka, ha - pa - ku - wa tu - ma -
break of day they doubt - ed; hope had va - nished; life had

Fine

- ri - ni.
pri - son.

Hal - le -
Al - le -

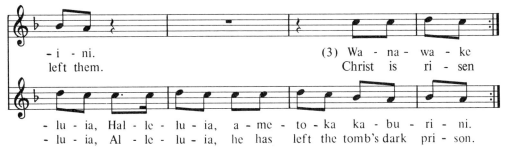

-i - ni.
left them.

(3) Wa - na - wa - ke
Christ is ri - sen

- lu - ia, Hal - le - lu - ia, a - me - to - ka ka - bu - ri - ni.
- lu - ia, Al - le - lu - ia, he has left the tomb's dark pri - son.

(Sw.) Joas Kijugo 1964
(E.) Erik Routley 1972

171

88

Tanzania
Traditional Melody
Harm. C.D.

Unison Solo (or semi-chorus)

1. M - fu - ra - hi - ni, Hal - le - lu - ya, M - ko - mbo - zi a -
1. He has a - ri - sen, Al - le - lu - ia! Re - joice and praise him;

- me - fu - fu - ka. A - me - fu - fu - ka, Hal - le - lu - ya. M - si - fu -
Al - le - lu - ia! For our Re - deem - er burst from the tomb, e - ven from

All

- ni sa - sa yu ha - i. Tu - mwi - mbi - e so - te kwa fu - ra -
death, dis - pel - ling its gloom. Let us sing praise to him with end - less

- ha. Ye - su a - me - to - ka ka - bu - ri - ni. Ka - shin - da
joy. Death's fear - ful sting he has come to de - stroy. Our sins for -

Ki - fo, Hal - le - lu - ya,   Hal - le - lu - ya, Ye - su yu ha - i.
- giv - ing, Al - le - lu - ia!   Je - sus is liv - ing, Al - le - lu - ia!

2. Amefufuka Mkombozi, / Halleluya, tushangilie. / Nguvu za mwovu ameshinda. / Ametuondoa kufani. / Tumwimbiesote . . .

3. Malaika aliwaambia / Wanawake, 'Msiogope. / Sasa kaburi lipo tupu, / Kwani Yesu amefufuka.' / Tumwimbiesote . . .

4. 'Amebatilisha Shetani. / Amewaletea wokovu. / Kwa hiyo ninyi mtangaze, / Ni hakika, Yesu yu hai.' / Tumwimbiesote . . .

Bernard Kyamanywa

2. For three long days the grave did its worst, / until its strength by God was dispersed. / He who gives life did death undergo, / and in its conquest his might did show. / Let us sing praise . . .

3. The angel said to them, 'Do not fear, / you look for Jesus who is not here. / See for yourselves, the tomb is all bare: / only the grave-clothes are lying there.' / Let us sing praise . . .

4. Go spread the news, he's not in the grave. / He has arisen, mankind to save. / Jesus' redeeming labours are done. / Even the battle with sin is won. / Let us sing praise . . .

Howard S. Olson 1969

89

Argentina
Pablo D. Sosa 1960
Harm. alt. C.D

a 4 **Central**

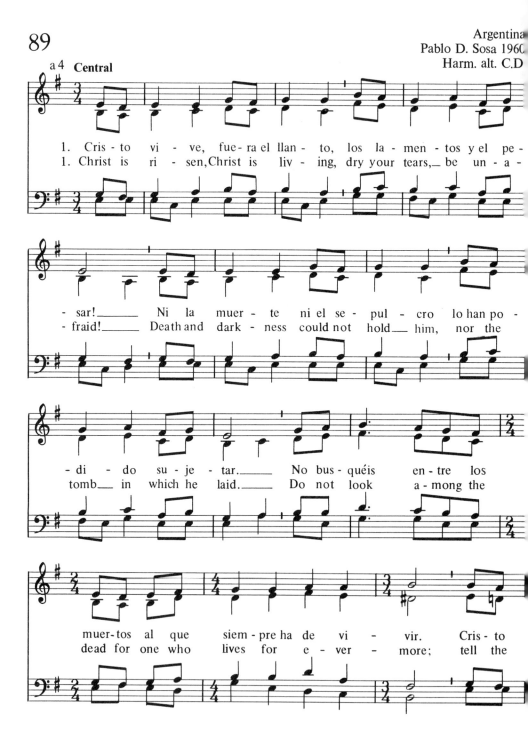

1. Cris - to vi - ve, fue - ra el llan - to, los la - men - tos y el pe -
1. Christ is ri - sen, Christ is liv - ing, dry your tears,— be un - a -

- sar!_____ Ni la muer - te ni el se - pul - cro lo han po -
- fraid!_____ Death and dark - ness could not hold__ him, nor the

- di - do su - je - tar._____ No bus - quéis en - tre los
tomb__ in which he laid._____ Do not look a - mong the

muer - tos al que siem - pre ha de vi - vir. Cris - to
dead for one who lives for e - ver - more; tell the

vi - ' ve! es - tas nue - vas por do - quier de - jad o - ir.
world that Christ is ri - sen, make it known he goes be - fore.

2. Que si Cristo no viviera / Vana fuera nuestra fe. / Mas se cumple su promesa: / 'Porque vivo, viviréis.' / Si en Adán entró la muerte, / por Jesús la vida entró; / No temáis, el triunfo es vuestro: / ¡El Señor resucitó!

3. Si es verdad que de la muerte / El pecado es aguijón, / No temáis pues Jesucristo / Nos da vida y salvación. / Gracias demos al Dios Padre / Que nos da seguridad, / Que quien cree en Jesucristo / Vive por la eternidad.

Nicolas Martinez 1960

2. If the Lord had never risen, / we'd have nothing to believe. / But his promise can be trusted: / 'You will live, because I live.' / As we share the death of Adam, / so in Christ we live again. / Death has lost its sting and terror. / Christ the Lord has come to reign.

3. Death has lost its old dominion, / let the world rejoice and shout! / Christ, the firstborn of the living / gives us life and leads us out. / Let us thank our God who causes / hope to spring up from the ground. / Christ is risen, Christ is giving / life eternal, life profound.

Fred Kaan 1972

90

Persia
Traditional Melody
Harm. C.D.

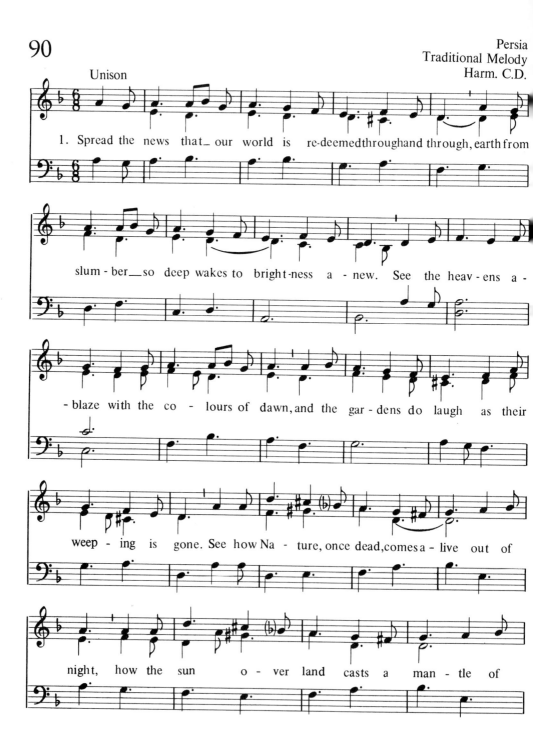

1. Spread the news that our world is re-deemed through and through, earth from

slum-ber so deep wakes to bright-ness a - new. See the heav-ens a -

- blaze with the co - lours of dawn, and the gar - dens do laugh as their

weep - ing is gone. See how Na - ture, once dead, comes a - live out of

night, how the sun o - ver land casts a man - tle of

light: For the Christ, who for us took the place of a

slave, gave us free-dom and life as he rose from the

grave: gave us free - dom and life as he rose from the grave.

2. Spread the news! look abroad! He has risen to reign! / Now at last heav'n is open'd to earth once again. / Now that death's power is spent and is vanquish'd for aye, / who should fear any storm, who now cringe in dismay? / Lift your eyes to the hills, greet the bright rising sun; / now our hearts and our souls are renewed all as one! / See, the tomb is found bare; this the work of God's hand; / see our Jesus now ris'n! In this faith may we stand: / see our Jesus now ris'n! In this faith may we stand!

Lewis Johnson 1969

(ویژه پرستش سپیده دم عید قیام)

۱ ـ مژده بادا که نو شد سراسر جهان! گشته بیدار گیتی ز خواب گران! بین چگونه شود رنگ رنگ آسمان! که کند گریه که خنده بر بوستان. بر طبیعت نگر مرده بد زنده شد! در جهان پرتو مهر تابنده شد. آن مسیحی که از بهر ما بنده شد، مرد و برخاست ما را رهاننده شد!

۲ ـ مژده آمد که اینک قیامش ببین! باز شدتا ابد آسمان بر زمین! موت دیگر نبد قدرتش بیش از این. از چه ترسم دگر از چه باشم حزین؟ سر بر آر از افق مهر تابان ما! بین چسان تازه گشته تن و جان ما! قبر خالی نگر! کار یزدان ما؟ زنده عیسی ببین! اصل ایمان ما.

Persian text by Hassan Dehqani (Anglican Church in Iran)

177

91

Germany
13th century melody
Harm. C.D.

Unison

1. Christ ist er-stan - den— von der Mar - ter al - le; des
2. Wär er nicht er-stan - den, so wär die Welt ver-gan - gen;
1. Christ is now ris'n a - gain— from his death and all his pain;
2. Had he not ris'n a - gain— we had been lost, this is plain;

soll'n wir al - le froh— sein,— Christ will un - ser Trost— sein.
seit daß er er-stan-den ist, so freut sich al - les, was da ist.
there-fore will we mer - ry be,— and re - joice with him glad - ly.
but since he is ris'n in - deed— let us love him with all speed.

Ky - ri - e - leis!
Ky - ri - e - leis!   3. Hal - le - lu - ja! Hal - le - lu - ja!
Ky - ri - e - leis!
Ky - ri - e - leis!   3. Al - le - lu - ia! Al - le - lu - ia!

Hal - le - lu - ja! Des soll'n wir al - le froh___ sein,
Al - le - lu - ia! There-fore will we mer - ry be,

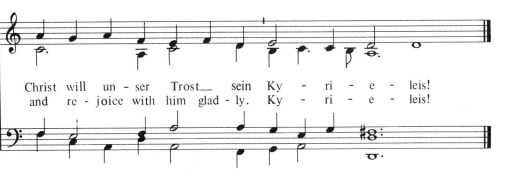

Christ will un - ser Trost___ sein Ky - ri - e - leis!
and re - joice with him glad - ly. Ky - ri - e - leis!

D. Anon. 13. Jh.
E. Miles Coverdale 1538

179

92

Unison

1. Christ lag in To-des-ban den, für un-ser Sünd ge-ge - ben,
1. Christ Je - sus lay in death's strong bands, for our of-fen - ces_ gi - ven,

der ist wie-der er-stan - den und hat uns bracht das_ Le - ben.
but now at God's right hand he stands and brings us life from hea - ven.

Des wir sol-len fröh-lich sein, Gott lo - ben und dank-bar sein,
Where-fore let us joy-ful be, and sing to God right thank-ful - ly

und sin-gen Hal-le-lu - ja! Hal-le-lu - ja!
loud songs of Al-le-lu - ia! Al-le-lu - ia!

2. Es war ein wunderlich Krieg, / da Tod und Leben rungen; / das Leben behielt den Sieg, / es hat den Tod verschlungen. / Die Schrift verkündet das, / wie ein Tod den andern fraß, / ein Spott aus dem Tod ist worden. / Halleluja!

3. So feiern wir das hohe Fest / mit Herzensfreud und Wonne, / das uns der Herr scheinen läßt, / er ist selber die Sonne. / Der durch seiner Gnaden Glanz, / erleucht' unsrer Herzen ganz, / der Sünden Nacht ist vergangen. / Halleluja!

Martin Luther 1524

2. It was a strange and dreadful strife, / when death and life contended. / The victory remained with life; / the reign of death was ended. / Stript of power no more he reigns, / an empty form alone remains; / his sting is lost for ever. / Alleluia!

3. So let us keep the festival / whereto the Lord invites us. / Christ is himself the joy of all, / the sun that warms and lights us. / By his grace he doth impart / eternal sunshine to the heart; / the night of sin is ended. / Alleluia!

R. Massie 1854

93

Germany and England
George Frederick Handel 1746

1. A toi la gloi - re, ô___ Res - sus - ci - té!
1. Yours be the glo - ry, yours_ O___ ri - sen friend!

A___ toi_ la vic - toi - re, pour l'é - ter - ni - té!
You_ have_won for e - ver vic - t'ry with - out end!

Bril - lant_ de lu - miè - re, l'ange est de - scen - du,
O___ how_ bright an an - gel rolls the stone a - way,

il ___ rou - le la pier - re du tom - beau vain - cu.
con - quer'd is the tomb in which your bo - dy lay.

A toi la gloi - re, ô__ Res - sus - ci - té!
Yours be the glo - ry, yours,. O_ ri - sen friend!

A__ toi_ la vic - toi - re pour l'é - ter - ni - té!
You_ have_ won for e - ver vic - t'ry with - out end.

2. Vois-le paraître, c'est lui, c'est Jésus, / ton Sauveur, ton Maître; Ôh! ne doute plus; / sois dans l'allégresse, peuple du Seigneur, / et redis sans cesse que Christ est vainqueur! / A toi la gloire, Ô Ressuscité! / A toi la victoire pour l'éternité.

3. Craindrais-je encore? Il vit à jamais, / celui que j'adore, le Prince de paix; / il est ma victoire, mon puissant soutien, / ma vie et ma gloire, non, je ne crains rien! / A toi la gloire, Ô Ressuscité! / A toi la victoire pour l'éternité.

Edmond Budry 1904

2. See, here is Jesus! who else could it be? / He, your Lord and Saviour, surely it is he! / Happy Church of Jesus, you who doubt no more, / never cease to tell us Christ is conqueror! / Yours be the glory, yours O risen Friend! / You have won for ever vict'ry without end.

3. He lives for ever! Bids me fear no more; / he is Prince of Peace! the one whom I adore. / With him to support me, vict'ry shall be won: / Now, my life, my glory, ev'ry fear is gone! / Yours be the glory, yours O risen Friend! / You have won for ever vict'ry without end.

F. Pratt Green 1971

94

a 4 **Easter Hymn**

1. Christ the Lord is ris'n to day.__ Al __ - le - lu - ia!

Sons of men and an - gels __ say: __ Al __ - le -

- lu - ia! Raise your joys and tri - umphs high:

Al __ - le - lu - ia! Sing,__ ye __ heav'ns, and __

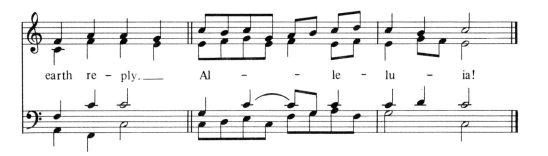

earth re - ply. ___ Al - - le - lu - ia!

2. Love's redeeming work is done. / Fought the fight, the battle won; /
Lo, our Sun's eclipse is o'er; / Lo, he sets in blood no more.

3. Vain the stone, the watch, the seal; / Christ has burst the gates of
hell; / Death in vain forbids him rise; / Christ has opened Paradise.

4. Lives again our glorious King; / Where, O Death, is now thy sting? /
Once he died our souls to save; / Where thy victory, O grave?

Charles Wesley 1739

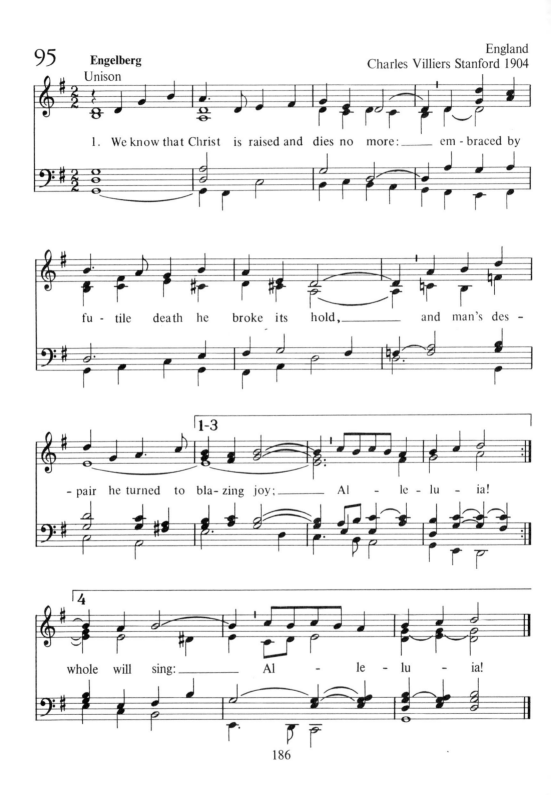

95 **Engelberg**

Unison

England
Charles Villiers Stanford 1904

1. We know that Christ is raised and dies no more:____ em - braced by
fu - tile death he broke its hold,____ and man's des -
- pair he turned to bla - zing joy;____ Al - le - lu - ia!
whole will sing:____ Al - le - lu - ia!

1-3

4

2. We share by water in his saving death: / this union brings to being one new cell, / a living and organic part of Christ: / Alleluia!

3. The Father's splendour clothes the Son with life: / the Spirit's fission shakes the Church of God: / baptized we live with God the Three in One: / Alleluia!

4. A new Creation comes to life and grows / as Christ's new body takes on flesh and blood: / the universe restored and whole will sing: / Alleluia!

John B. Geyer 1964

96

France
Jean Langlais 1957

Prelude (v. 1)

Refrain
℅ Unison

1. Dieu, nous a-vons vu ta
1. God, your glo-ry we have

gloire en ton Christ, plein de grâce et de vé-ri-
seen in your Son, full of truth, full of heav'n-ly

-té, en lui fais nous vi-vre, pleins de cha-ri-té
grace: in Christ make us live,— his love shine on our face,

et le mon-de ver-ra les fruits de ta vic-toi-re.
and the na-tions shall see in us the tri-umph you have won.

Fine

188

1. Le Sei - gneur a je - té la pa - role__ au sil - lon. Il
1. In the fields of this world his good news__ he has sown, and

a se - mé la graine. Il at - tend__ la mois - son.
sends us out to reap till the har - vest is done.

2. Le Seigneur a passé comme un feu dévorant. / Il a lancé la braise. Il attend nos sarments.

3. Le Seigneur s'est livré pour la Pâque en son Corps; / il a rompu le pain. Il attend notre mort.

4. Le Seigneur a foulé le raisin sur la Croix, / il a rempli la coupe, il attend notre joie.

5. Le Seigneur a construit un Royaume nouveau, / il a taillé le pierre. Il attend nos travaux.

Didier Rimaud 1957

2. In his love like a fire that consumes he pass'd by; / the flame has touched our lips; let us shout, 'Here am I!'

3. He was broken for us, God-forsaken his cry, / and still the bread he breaks: to ourselves we must die.

4. He has trampled the grapes of new life on his Cross; / now drink the cup and live: he has filled it for us.

5. He has founded a kingdom that none shall destroy; / the corner-stone is laid. Go to work: build with joy!

Refrain: Sir Ronald Johnson 1964
Verses: Brian Wren 1964

97 **Christe Sanctorum**
Unison

1. Christ is the world's light; he and none o - ther; born in our dark - ness, he be-came our bro - ther. If we have seen him, we have seen the Fa - ther: Glo - ry to God on high!

2. Christ is the world's peace: / he and none other; / no man can serve him / and despise his brother. / Who else unites us / one in God the Father? / Glory to God on high!

3. Christ is the world's life, / he and none other; / sold once for silver, / murdered here, our Brother– / he, who redeems us, / reigns with God the Father: / Glory to God on high!

4. Give God the glory, / God and none other; / give God the glory, Spirit, Son and Father; / give God the glory, / God in man my brother: / Glory to God on high!

F. Pratt Green 1968

98

France
Dominique Ombrie 1963

Gloire à toi, Jé - sus Christ, __ Sei - gneur res - sus - ci -
Praise to you, Je - sus Christ, __ you __ are our ri - sen

- té, tu nous don - nes la vie; Gloire à toi, Jé - sus
Lord; you have giv'n __ us new life: Praise to you, Je - sus

Christ, __ tu __ viens nous li - bé - rer; tu es notre U - ni - té.
Christ, __ you __ came to set us free; you are our U - ni - ty.

[continued overleaf

Verses

1. Tu es la vraie lu - miè - re jail - lie dans no - tre
2. Vic - toi - re qui dé - li - vre des mar - ques du pé -
1. The cloud of cha - os parts___ riv'n by the light of
2. Your Pas - sion gives new life___ to men now born a -

nuit, prin - temps de no - tre ter - re c'est toi qui nous con - duis.
- ché, ta pâ - ques nous fait vi - vre en vrais res - sus - ci - tés.
truth; where walks the ri - sen Lord__ old earth re - news her youth.
- gain; and your com - man - ding touch__ e - ra - ses sin's deep stain.

3. Parole vivifiante, / tu viens pour notre faim; / dans notre longue attente, / ton corps est notre pain.

4. Tu fais de nous des frères / rassemblés par ta Croix. / Enfants d'un même Père, / nous partageons ta joie.

5. Merveille de ta grâce, / tu viens nous libérer. / Qu'en ton amour se fasse, / Seigneur, notre unité.   Dominique Ombrie 1963

3. You, God's life-giving Word / still come our minds to feed, / to waiting wanderers still / you give the living Bread.

4. Your friends are drawn to you / where you are lifted up, / one family of God, / one faith, one joy, one hope!

5. Amazing love! You came / to set your people free. / Now may this love call forth / your people's unity.   Erik Routley 1972

192

99

England
Psalmodia Evangelica 1789
Harm. English Hymnal 1906

Truro

1. Je - sus shall reign wher - e'er the sun does his suc - ces - sive jour - neys run; his king-dom stretch from shore to shore, till moons shall wax and wane no more.

2. People and realms of every tongue / dwell on his love with sweetest song, / and infant voices shall proclaim / their early blessings on his name.

3. Blessings abound where'er he reigns; / the prisoner leaps to lose his chains; / the weary find eternal rest, / and all the sons of want are blest.

4. Let every creature rise and bring / peculiar honours to our King; / angels descend with songs again, / and earth repeat the long amen.

Isaac Watts 1719

The Holy Spirit and the Word of God
Der Heilige Geist und das Wort Gottes
Le Saint-Esprit et la Parole de Dieu

100a

Veni Creator
Unison

Europe
Vatican Plainsong melody
Mode vii

1. Ve - ni Cre - a - tor___ Spi - ri - tus,
1. Come, O Cre - a - tor___ Spi - rit, come,

men - tes tu - o - rum___ vi - si - ta
and make with - in our___ hearts thy home;

im - ple___ su - per - na___ gra - ti - a
to us___ thy___ grace___ ce - les - tial give,

quae___ tu___ cre - as - ti pec - to - ra.
who___ of___ thy___ breath - ing move and live.

194

100b

Veni Creator

1. Ve - ni Cre - a - tor Spi - ri - tus, men - tes tu -
1. Come, O Cre - a - tor Spi - rit, come, and make with -

- o - rum vi - si - ta im - ple su - per - na gra -
- in our hearts thy home; to us thy grace ce - les -

- ti - a quae tu cre - as - ti pec - to - ra.
- tial give, who of thy breath - ing move and live.

2. Accende lumen sensibus / infund'amorem cordibus, / infirma nostri corporis / virtute firmans perpeti.

3. Hostem repellas longius, / pacemque dones protinus; / ductore sic te praevio, / vitemus omne noxium.

4. Per te sciamus da Patrem, / noscamus atque Filium, / teque utriusque Spiritum / credamus omni tempore.

9th century

2. Our senses with thy light inflame, / our hearts to heavenly love reclaim; / our bodies' poor infirmity / with strength perpetual fortify.

3. Our mortal foe afar repel, / grant us henceforth in peace to dwell; / and so to us, with thee for guide / no ill shall come, no harm betide.

4. May we by thee the Father learn / and know the Son, and thee discern, / who art of both and thus adore / in perfect faith for evermore.

Robert Bridges 1899

Germany
Later form of melody in
Encheiridion 1524
Harm. C.D.

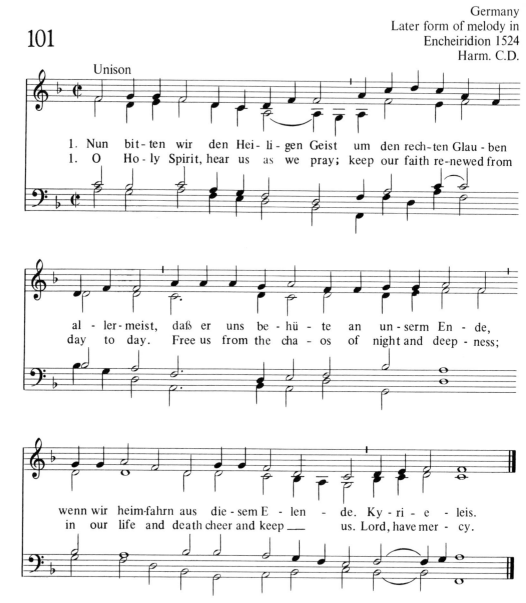

Unison

1. Nun bit-ten wir den Hei- li-gen Geist um den rech-ten Glau-ben
1. O Ho-ly Spirit, hear us as we pray; keep our faith re-newed from

al - ler-meist, daß er uns be-hü - te an un-serm En - de,
day to day. Free us from the cha - os of night and deep - ness;

wenn wir heim-fahrn aus die-sem E - len - de. Ky-ri-e - leis.
in our life and death cheer and keep ___ us. Lord, have mer - cy.

196

2. Du wertes Licht, gib uns deinen Schein, / lehr uns Jesus Christ kennen allein, / daß wir an ihm bleiben, dem treuen Heiland, / der uns bracht hat zum rechten Vaterland. / Kyrieleis.

3. Du süße Lieb, schenk uns deine Gunst, / laß uns empfinden der Liebe Glut, / daß wir uns von Herzen einander lieben / und im Frieden auf einem Sinn bleiben. / Kyrieleis.

Martin Luther 1524

2. Uproot and teach us by your restless love, / help us to share all that we are and have, / that with strong affection, in truth and doing, / we may love all men, peace pursuing. / Lord, have mercy.

3. You plead our cause, and by your gift of peace / life is from the fear of death released. / How we need your presence, O gift from heaven, / all our words and deeds to enliven. / Lord have mercy.

Fred Kaan 1968, 1972

102

England
Ralph Vaughan Williams 1906

Down Ampney

a 4

1. Come down, O Love— di - vine, seek thou this soul— of—

mine, and vi - sit it with thine own ar - dour— glow - ing;

O Com - for - ter,— draw— near, with - in my heart— ap -

- pear, and— kin - dle it, thy— ho - ly flame be - stow - ing.

2. O let it freely burn, / till earthly passions turn / to dust and ashes in its heat consuming; / and let thy glorious light / shine ever on my sight, / and clothe me round, the while my path illuming.

3. Let holy charity / my outward vesture be, / and lowliness become mine inner clothing; / true lowliness of heart, / which takes the humbler part, / and o'er its own shortcomings weeps with loathing.

4. And so the yearning strong, / with which the soul will long / shall far outpass the power of human telling; / for none can guess its grace, / till he become the place / wherein the Holy Spirit makes his dwelling.

Bianco da Siena, d. 1434
tr. R. F. Littledale 1867

198

103

Germany
H. R. Siemoneit 1964

Introduction (v. 1 only)

Unison

1. Wir bit - ten, Herr, um dei - nen Geist, daß du uns dei - ne Kraft ver-
1. We would ask, Lord,— for your Spi - rit! It is he who gives us your

- leihst! Daß wir das Al - te neu ver-ste-hen und uns__ in Got- tes Nä - he
strength. So__ we new-ly un-der-stand__ the old __ and find that God is

se - hen. Wir bit - ten, Herr, um dei - nen Geist!
near us. We would ask, Lord,____ for your Spi - rit!

199

[vv. 2, 3 overleaf

2. Wir bitten, Herr, um deinen Geist, / daß du uns deine Kraft verleihst! / Wir wollen nicht nur Fragen nennen, / wir möchten auch die Antwort kennen. / Wir bitten, Herr, um deinen Geist!

3. Wir bitten, Herr, um deinen Geist, / daß du uns deine Kraft verleihst! / Auch wenn wir fürchten zu versagen, / so laß uns doch die Antwort wagen. / Wir bitten, Herr, um deinen Geist!

Dieter Trautwein 1964

2. We would ask, Lord, for your Spirit! / It is he who gives us your strength. / We don't want just to ask the questions, / we want to know the answer. / We would ask, Lord, for your Spirit!

3. We would ask, Lord, for your Spirit! / It is he who gives us your strength. / Though we are frightened we might lose heart, / we still may risk the answer. / We would ask, Lord, for your Spirit!

F. Pratt Green 1973

104

Nigeria
Yoruba tune
Fela Sowande 1969

1. Bles-sed Word of God, ___ bles-sed Word of God, light of the

fal - ter - ing steps of men, bles - sed Word of God.

2. Holy Word of God, / holy Word of God, / drawing our hearts up to
God above, / holy Word of God.

3. Sweetest Word of God, / sweetest Word of God, / message of love
coming down from heav'n, / sweetest Word of God.

4. Word of sins forgiven, / word of sins forgiven, / word of salvation's
redeeming love, / word of sins forgiven.

5. Word of truth and life, / word of truth and life, / teaching of Jesus, our
way and guide, / word of truth and life.

6. Joyous Word of God, / joyous Word of God, / leading us all to the
joys of heav'n, / joyous Word of God.

A. M. Jones 1969

105

Belgium
Jean van der Cauter 1965

1. Es - prit, toi qui gui - des tous les hom - mes, gar - de -
1. Good Spi - rit of God, guide of your chil - dren, keep them

- les pour la gloi - re du Pè - re; u - nis -
all for the glo - ry of the Fa - ther; keep them

- les dans ton peu - ple de la ter - re; con - duis -
all in the love of one an - oth - er; lead them

- les par la rou - te qui mè - ne au Roy - au - me.
all in the quest for the ho - nour of the King - dom.

Gui - de - nous sur les rou - tes de la ter - re,
Be our guide through this pil - gri - mage of liv - ing,

con - duis - nous vers les hom - mes, nos frè - res.
turn us each to his bro - ther in self - gi - ving.

2. Esprit, toi qui souffles sur le monde, / brûle-nous de ta flamme si claire; / purifie tous nos gestes de misère; / conduis-nous où la grâce du Christ surabonde. / Guide-nous sur les routes de la terre, / conduis-nous vers les hommes, nos frères.

3. Esprit, toi que donnes la justice, / donne-nous de combattre la haine; / force-nous à défendre ceux qui peinent, / conduis-nous vers les pauvres qui sont ton Eglise. / Guide-nous sur les routes de la terre, / conduis-nous vers les hommes, nos frères.

Didier Rimaud 1965

2. Pure Spirit of God, fresh wind of blessing, / let your fire in its energy inflame us; / let your healing from misery reclaim us; / lead us all where the faithful Christ's grace are confessing. / Be our guide through this pilgrimage of living, / turn us each to his brother in self-giving.

3. Great Spirit of God, source of all justice, / in your war against hatred keep us faithful; / in protecting the poor keep us watchful; / in our search for the household of peace still protect us. / Be our guide through this pilgrimage of living, / turn us each to his brother in self-giving.

Erik Routley 1972

106

1. 世 の な か に ふ み ちょう ふ み は
1. In this world a - bound ____ scrolls of wis - dom _ num - ber - less,

お お け れ ど ま こ と の ふ み は
but the pu - rest _ truth ____ in the Word of God is _ found; _

み ふ み な り け り み ふ み な り け り
this the book that points the way _ trod by the sa - ges _ long _ a - go. ____

2. いにしえの　聖徒のふみし
　　　そのあとも。
　　さやかにしめす　ふみや、このふみ。

3. くりかえし　またくりかえし
　　　ひもとけど、
　つきぬはかみの　まことなりけり。

4. うえもなき　まことのみちの
　　　かしこさは、
　ふみてのちてそ　しるべかりけり。

Saichiro Yuya 1864–1941

2. Study as we may, never can we grasp thereby / all the depth of truth;
we must ever watch and pray, / walking on the holy way trod by the
sages long ago.

Esther Hibbard 1962

107

Cartigny

a 4

1. Ta voix, mon Dieu, a dit ___ mon nom. Ta
1. Your voice, my God, calls me ___ by name; your

joie m'at-tend ___ dans ta mai - son. Ta Pa - ro - le,
joy a - waits ___ me in your home. Dear - est Lord, your

mon ___ Sei-gneur, est fi - dè - le, ___ é - ter - nel - le.
kind - ly word fails me ne - ver, ___ stands for e - ver. ___

2. Ta mort, Jésus, m'a délivré. / Tu vis en moi ressuscité. / Ta Parole,
mon Seigneur / est vivante, agissante.

3. Esprit d'amour, redis ce mot / qui crée en moi un cœur nouveau. / Ta
Parole, mon Seigneur, / est lumière et prière.

Claude Rozier 1957

2. Your death, my Jesus, sets me free; / your life has risen again in me. /
Dearest Lord, your vital word / activates me, captivates me.

3. Spirit of love, repeat that sign / which makes anew this heart of
mine. / Dearest Lord, now is your word / shining o'er me, praying for me.

F. Pratt Green 1972

205

The Church · Its Worship and Praise
Die Kirche · Gottesdienst und Lobpreisung
L'Eglise · Adoration et Louange

108

Germany
Stralsund Gesangbuch 1665

1. Lo - be den Her - ren, den mäch- ti - gen Kö - nig der Eh -
1. Praise to the Lord! the al - migh- ty, the King of cre - a -

- ren! Mei - ne ge - lie - be - te See - le, das ist mein Be -
- tion! O my soul, praise him, for he is thy health and sal -

- geh - ren. Kom-met zu Hauf! Psal - ter und
- va - tion! All ye who hear, now to his

Har - fe,— wacht auf! Las - set den Lob - ge -sang hö - ren!
tem - ple — draw near, serve him in glad a - do - ra - tion!

2. Lobe den Herren, der alles so herrlich regieret, / der dich auf Adelers Fittichen sicher geführet, / der dich erhält, / wie es dir selber gefällt. / Hast du nicht dieses verspüret?

3. Lobe den Herren, der deinen Stand sichtbar gesegnet, / der aus dem Himmel mit Strömen der Liebe geregnet. / Denke daran, / was der Allmächtige kann, / der dir mit Liebe begegnet!

4. Lobe den Herren, was in mir ist lobe den Namen. / Lob ihn mit allen, die seine Verheissung bekamen. / Er ist dein Licht; / Seele, vergiss es ja nicht. / Lob ihn in Ewigkeit! Amen!

Joachim Neander 1650–1680

2. Praise to the Lord! Who o'er all things so wondrously reigneth, / shielding thee gently from harm and from fainting sustaineth; / hast thou not seen / how thy desires have been / granted in what He ordaineth?

3. Praise to the Lord! Who doth prosper thy work and defend thee, / surely his goodness and mercy here daily attend thee; / ponder anew / what the Almighty can do, / if with His love He befriend thee!

4. Praise to the Lord! Oh let all that is in me adore Him! / All that hath life and breath come now with praises before Him! / Let the Amen / sound from His people again, / gladly for aye we adore Him.

C. Winkworth 1858

109

Germany
Kölner Gesangbuch 1623
Harm. Ralph Vaughan Williams 1906

Lasst uns erfreuen

Unison

1. From all that dwell be - low the skies let the cre - a-tor's praise a -
2. E - ter-nal are thy mer-cies, Lord: e - ter - nal truth at-tends thy

a 4   Unison

- rise.   Al - le - lu - ia!   Al - le - lu - ia!   Let
word.   Al - le - lu - ia!   Al - le - lu - ia!   Thy

the Re-deem - er's Name be sung   through ev' - ry land in ev' - ry
praise shall sound from shore to shore,   till   suns shall rise and set no

tongue.   Al - le - lu - ia,   Al - le - lu - ia,   Al - le -
more.   Al - le - lu - ia,   Al - le - lu - ia,   Al - le -

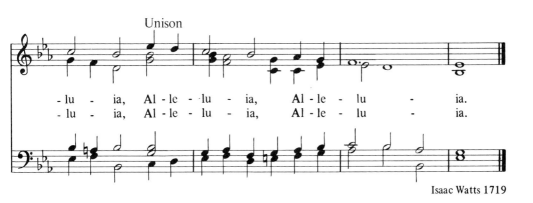

Unison

-lu - ia, Al - le - lu - ia,   Al - le - lu - ia.
-lu - ia, Al - le - lu - ia,   Al - le - lu - ia.

Isaac Watts 1719

209

110

1. Nun dan-ket al-le Gott mit Her-zen, Mund und Hän - den.
1. Now thank we all our God, with heart and hands and voi - ces,

Der gro-ße Din-ge tut an uns und al-len En - den,
who wond-rous things hath done, in whom his world re-joi - ces;

der uns von Mut-ter-leib und Kin-des-bei-nen an,
who from our mo-ther's arms hath blessed us on our way

un-zäh-lig viel zu gut, und __ noch jetz und ge - tan.
with count-less gifts of love, and __ still is ours to - day.

2. Der ewigreiche Gott / woll uns in unserm Leben / ein immer fröhlich Herz / und edlen Frieden geben / und uns in seiner Gnad / erhalten fort und fort / und uns aus aller Not / erlösen hier und dort.

3. Lob, Ehr und Preis sei Gott / dem Vater und dem Sohne / und Gott dem Heilgen Geist / im höchsten Himmelsthrone, / ihm, dem dreieinen Gott, / wie es im Anfang war / und ist und bleiben wird / so jetzt und immerdar.

Martin Rinckart, 1636, Ecclus 50
22-4 and Gloria

2. O may this bounteous God / through all our life be near us, / with ever joyful hearts / and blessed peace to cheer us, / and keep us in his grace, / and guide us when perplexed, / and free us from all ills / in this world and the next.

3. All praise and thanks to God / the Father now be given, / the Son, and Him who reigns / with them in highest heaven, / the one eternal God, / whom earth and heaven adore; / for thus it was, is now, / and shall be evermore.

Catherine Winkworth 1858

111

Lasst uns erfreuen

Germany
Kölner Gesangbuch 1623
Harm. Ralph Vaughan Williams 1906

1. All crea-tures of our God and King, lift up your voice and with us sing Al-le-lu - ia, Al-le-lu - ia! Thou burn-ing sun with gold-en beam, thou sil-ver moon with soft-er gleam, Al-le-lu - ia, Al-le-lu - ia! O___

212

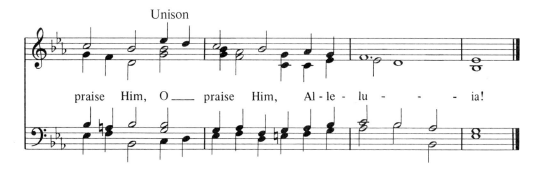

praise Him, O praise Him, Al-le-lu - - - ia!

2. Thou rushing wind that art so strong, / ye clouds that sail in heav'n along, / Alleluia, Alleluia! / Thou rising morn, in praise rejoice, / ye lights of evening, find a voice, / Alleluia, Alleluia! / O praise Him, O praise Him, Alleluia!

3. Thou flowing water, pure and clear, / make music for thy Lord to hear, / Alleluia, Alleluia! / Thou fire so masterful and bright, / that givest man both warmth and light, / Alleluia, Alleluia! / O praise Him, O praise Him, Alleluia!

4. Dear mother earth, who day by day / unfoldest blessings on our way, / Alleluia, Alleluia! / The flowers and fruit that in Thee grow, / let them His glory also show, / Alleluia, Alleluia! / O praise Him, O praise Him, Alleluia!

5. And ye all men of tender heart, / forgiving others, take your part, / Alleluia, Alleluia! / Ye, who long pain and sorrow bear, / praise God and on Him cast your care, / Alleluia, Alleluia! / O praise Him, O praise Him, Alleluia!

6. And thou most kind and gentle Death, / waiting to hush our latest breath, / Alleluia, Alleluia! / Thou leadest home the child of God, / and Christ our Lord the way hath trod, / Alleluia, Alleluia! / O praise Him, O praise Him, Alleluia!

7. Let all things their Creator bless, / and worship Him in humbleness, / Alleluia, Alleluia! / Praise, praise the Father, praise the Son, / and praise the Spirit, Three in One, / Alleluia, Alleluia! / O praise Him, O praise Him, Alleluia!

St. Francis of Assisi 1182-1226
tr. W. H. Draper, about 1913

112

Cameroun
Abel Nkuinji 1970
Harm. C.D.

1. Tout est fait pour la gloi-re de Dieu, A - men! A - men!
2. La vie c'est pour la gloi-re de Dieu, A - men! A - men!
3. Le culte est pour la gloi-re de Dieu, A - men! A - men!
4. Le prin-temps pour la gloi-re de Dieu, A - men! A - men!
5. L'offrande est pour la gloi-re de Dieu, A - men! A - men!

1.—5. Tout dé-pend de ce que tu en fais. A - men! A -

- men! A - men! A - men! A - men!

Tout est fait pour la gloi-re de Dieu, A - men! A - men!

113

Germany
Dieter Hechtenberg 1969

1. Singt das Lied der Freu- de ü - ber Gott!
1. Sing for joy! Sing prai -ses to the Lord!

Lobt ihn laut, der euch er-schaf-fen hat!
Praise his name, the Fa -ther of us all!

Preist ihn, hel - le Ster - ne, lobt ihn, Son - ne, Mond,
Praise him, shin -ing pla - nets, praise him, moon and sun,

[continued overleaf

215

auch im Welt-all fer — ne sei-ne Eh re wohnt.
praise him, far-thest spa — ces, a-toms one by one.

Singt das Lied der Freu-de ü-ber Gott!
Sing for joy! Sing prai-ses to the Lord!

2. Singt das Lied der Freude über Gott! / Lobt ihn laut, der euch erschaffen hat! / Preist ihn, ihr Gewitter, Hagel, Schnee und Wind. / Lobt ihn alle Tiere, die auf Erden sind. / Singt das Lied der Freude über Gott!

3. Singt das Lied der Freude über Gott! / Lobt ihn laut, der euch erschaffen hat. / Stimmt mit ein, ihr Menschen, preist ihn Gross und Klein, / seine Hoheit rühmen soll ein Fest euch sein! / Singt das Lied der Freude über Gott.

4. Singt das Lied der Freude über Gott! / Lobt ihn laut, der euch erschaffen hat. / Er wird Kraft uns geben, Glanz und Licht wird sein, / in das dunkle Leben leuchtet hell sein Schein: / Singt das Lied der Freude über Gott.

Dieter Hechtenberg 1969

2. Sing for joy! Sing praises to the Lord! / Praise his name, the Father of us all! / Praise him, rolling thunder, hail and wind and snow, / praise him, ev'ry creature, moving fast or slow. / Sing for joy! Sing praises to the Lord!

3. Sing for joy! Sing praises to the Lord! / Praise his name, the Father of us all! / Join in, every nation, praise him great and small, / join the celebration! He is Lord of all! / Sing for joy! Sing praises to the Lord!

4. Sing for joy! Sing praises to the Lord! / Praise his name, the Father of us all! / He will send his spirit, day will break on night, / He will give us power, freedom, love and light! / Sing for joy! Sing praises to the Lord!

Emily Chisholm 1972

114

Japan
Isao Koizumi 1958

1. Se - ka - i no to - mo to te o tsu - na - gi,
1. Here, O Lord, thy ser - vants ga - ther, hand we link with hand:

Ju - ji - ka no mo - to ni ta - tsu wa - re - ra,
look - ing t'ward our Sa - viour's cross___ joined in love we stand.

Ka - mi no mi - ku - ni o me - a - te to shi,
As we seek the realm of God___ we u - nite to pray:

Shu Ie - su no mi - chi___ o su - su - mi - yu kan.
Je - sus, Sa - viour guide our steps___ for you are the Way.

2. Kuni to kotobaba wa kotonaredo, / Kokoro wa onaji Shu no tamu zo. / Kuraki jidai no nozomi naru, / Shu Iesu no makoto hiromeyukan.

3. Uchuu no himitsu saguru tomo, / tokiwa no heiwa nas tooshi. / Tsukare itameru hitobito ni. / Shu Iesu no inochi wakachiyukan.

4. Michi to makoto to inochi naru, / Shu Iesu o tsune no aogitsutsu, / ai ni motozuku tsugi no yo o, / chukara o awase kizukiyukan.

Tokuo Yamaguchi 1958

2. Many are the tongues we speak, scatter'd are the lands, / yet our hearts are one in God and his love's demands. / Ev'n in darkness hope appears calling age and youth: / Jesus, Teacher, dwell with us, for you are the Truth.

3. Nature's secrets open wide, changes never cease; / where, O where can weary men find the source of peace? / Unto all those sore distressed, torn by endless strife, / Jesus, healer, bring your balm, for you are the Life.

4. Grant, O Lord, an age renewed, filled with deathless love; / help us as we work and pray, send us from above / truth and courage, faith and power needed in our strife: / Jesus, Christ, you are our Way, you our Truth, our Life.

E. M. Stowe 1958 altd.

115

Unison

1. Her - re Gud, ditt dy - re navn og ae – re
1. Migh - ty God, to thy dear name be gi – ven

o - ver ver - den høit i akt skal vae - re, og
high-est praise in all the earth and hea - ven. All

al - le sje - le, de tret - te trae - le, alt
souls dis - tressed,____ all men op - pressed,____ their

som har mae - le, de skal for - tel — le din ae — re.
voi - ces rais - ing u - nite in prais - ing thy glo — ry.

2. Gud er Gud, om alle land lå øde, / Gud er Gud, om alle mann var
døde. / Om slekter svimler Blandt Stjernestimler / i høie himler Utallig
vrimler Guds grøde.

3. Høie hall og dype dal skal vike. / Jord og himmel falle skal tillike. /
Hvert fjell, hver tinde skal brått forsvinne, / men opp skal rinne, som
solen skinne Guds rike!

Petter Dass 1640-1707

2. God is God, tho' all the earth lay wasted; / God is God, though all
men death had tasted. / While nations stumble, in darkness fumble, / by
stars surrounded countless aboundeth God's harvest.

3. Highest hills and deepest vales shall vanish, / earth and heaven both
alike be banished, / as in the dawning of ev'ry morning, / the sun
appeareth so glorious neareth God's kingdom.

Eivind Berggrav 1951/2

116

Carolyn

a 4

1. God of love and truth and beau-ty, Hal-low'd be thy name; ___

fount of or-der, law and du-ty, Hal-low'd be thy name. ___

As in heav'n thy hosts a-dore thee, and their fa-ces veil be-fore thee,

so on earth, Lord, we im-plore thee, Hal-low'd be thy name. ___

222

2. Lord, remove our guilty blindness, / Hallowed be thy name; / show thy heart of lovingkindness, / Hallowed be thy name. / By our hearts' deep-felt contrition, / by our minds' enlighten'd vision, / by our wills' complete submission, / Hallow'd be thy name.

3. In our worship, Lord most holy, / Hallow'd be thy name; / in our work, however lowly, / Hallow'd be thy name; / in each heart's imagination, / in the Church's adoration, / in the conscience of the nation, / Hallow'd be thy name.

Timothy Rees 1922

223

117

Nigeria
Olajida Olude 1964
Harm. C.D.

1. Je - su, a fé pa- dé o L'ọ - jọ — Rẹ t'a-jo mí-mọ
1. Je - sus, we want — to meet on this — your ho - ly day.

Drum beat etc.

A sì y'i - te Rẹ ka o L'ọ - jọ — Rẹ t'a-jo mí-mọ
We ga - ther round your throne on this — your ho - ly day.

I - wọ ọ - rẹ wa ọ - run A - du- rà wa mbọ wa o,
You — are — our heav' - nly friend: our — prayers are on their way,

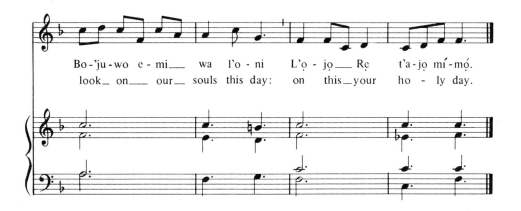

Bo-'ju-wo e - mi___ wa l'o - ni L'ọ - jọ___ Rẹ ___ t'a - jọ mí - mọ́.
look___ on___ our___ souls this day: on this___your ho - ly day.

2. L'erù l'a kunlè ki O, L'Ojo Re t' àjo mímó; / A sì fe k' Iwo ko 'ni L' Ojo Re t' àjo mímó; / Gbà wa là, s' okàn wa d' otun Sàkoso 'se sin yi o, / Bus' èso 'Gbàgbo wa, dakun L' Ojo Re t' àjo mímó.

3. Jesù, a de, bùkun ni l' Ojo Re t' àjo mímó. / F' ayò 'segun Re fun ni, L' Ojo Re t' àjo mímó / Atilà nihin j' èbùn Re, Kà wa ye fun yè, nihín / A fe okàn bi ti Kristì L' Ojo Re t' àjo mímó.

4. L' okàn kan, k' a son l' èye L' Ojo Re t' àjo mímó; / Okan 'lora kò dara, L' Ojo Re t' àjo mímó; / F' Em' Igbàgbo so ni d' òtun Bùkun waasù nihin; / Gbà a nlo, sìn wa lo, Oluwa K' a je Tìre, Tire lai, se.

Olajida Olude 1964

2. We greet you on our knees on this your holy day, / and would be taught by you on this your holy day. / Save us and make us new: lead and guide our songs of praise: / Make the seed of faith to grow, we pray, on this your holy day.

3. Your blessing, Lord, we seek on this your holy day; / give joy of victory on this your holy day. / Through grace alone are we saved; in your flock may we be found; / let the mind of Christ abide in us on this your holy day!

4. Our minds we dedicate on this your holy day; / heart and soul consecrate on this your holy day. / Holy Spirit, make us whole; bless the worship in this place, / and as we go from it, lead us, Lord: we are yours evermore.

Biodun Adebesin and Austin Lovelace 1966

225

118

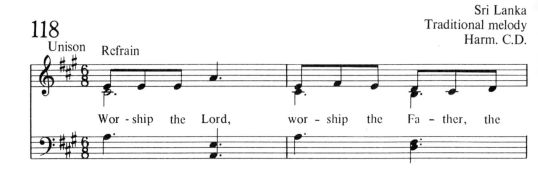

Unison Refrain

Wor - ship the Lord, wor - ship the Fa - ther, the

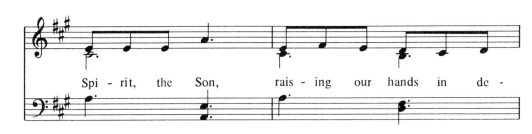

Spi - rit, the Son, rais - ing our hands in de -

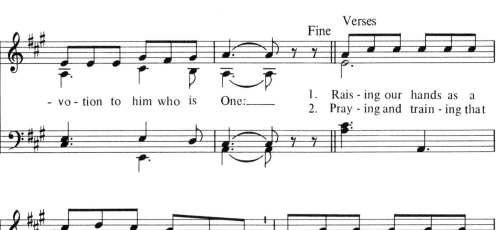

Fine Verses

- vo - tion to him who is One:____

1. Rais - ing our hands as a
2. Pray - ing and train - ing that

sign of re - joi - cing and with our lips our to -
we be a bless - ing and by our work - man - ship

-ge - ther - ness voi - cing giv - ing our - selves to a
dai - ly ex - press - ing we are com - mit - ted to

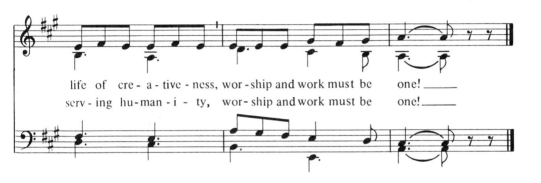

life of cre - a - tive - ness, wor - ship and work must be one!____
serv - ing hu - man - i - ty, wor - ship and work must be one!____

3. Called to be partners with God in creation, / honouring Christ as the Lord of the nation, / we must be ready for risk and for sacrifice, / worship and work must be one!

4. Bringing the bread and the wine to the table, / asking that we may be led and enabled, / truly united, to find a new brotherhood, / worship and work must be one!

5. Now in response to the life you are giving, / help us, O Father, to offer our living, / seeking a just and a healing society, / worship and work must be one!

Fred Kaan 1972

227

119

Germany
N. Decius 1529
Harm. C.D.

1. Al - lein ___ Gott in der Höh' sei Ehr und
1. All glo - ry be to God on high, who

Dank ___ für sei - ne Gna - de, dar - um, ___ daß nun und
hath ___ our race ___ be - friend - ed! To us ___ no harm shall

nim - mer - mehr uns rüh - ren kann ___ kein Scha - de. Ein
now ___ come nigh, the strife at last ___ has end - ed. God

Wohl - ge - falln Gott an ___ uns hat; nun ist ___ groß Fried ohn
show - eth his good - will ___ to men, and peace ___ shall reign on

Un - ter - laß, all Fehd hat nun___ ein En - de.
earth___ a - gain; O thank him for___ his good - ness!

2. Wir loben, preisn, anbeten dich; / für deine Ehr wir danken, / dass du,
Gott Vater ewiglich / regierst ohn alles Wanken. / Ganz ungemessn ist
deine Macht, / fort g'schieht, was dein Will hat bedacht: / wohl uns des
feinen Herren!

3. O Jesu Christ, Sohn eingeborn, / deines himmlischen Vaters, /
Versöhner der', die warn verlorn, / du Stiller unsers Haders, / Lamm
Gottes, heilger Herr und Gott: / nimm an die Bitt von unsrer Not, /
erbarm dich unser aller.

4. O Heilger Geist, du höchstes Gut, / du alterheilsamst' Tröster, / vor
Teufels Gwalt fortan behüt, / die Jesus Christ erlöset / durch grosse
Martr und bittern Tod; / abwend all unsern Jammr und Not! / Darauf wir
uns verlassen!

N. Decius 1480–1529

2. We praise, we worship thee, we trust / and give thee thanks for ever, /
O Father, that thy reign is just / and wise and changes never. / Thy
boundless power o'er all things reigns, / done is whate'er thy will
ordains: / well for us that thou reignest!

3. O Jesus Christ, thou only Son / of God, thy heavenly Father, / who
didst for all our sins atone / and thy lost sheep dost gather; / thou Lamb
of God, to thee on high / from out our depths we sinners cry - / have
mercy on us, Jesus!

4. O Holy Ghost, thou precious Gift, / thou comforter unfailing, / o'er
Satan's snares our souls uplift / and let thy power availing / avert our
woes and calm our dread: / for us the Saviour's blood was shed; / we
trust in thee to save us.

C. Winkworth 1863

120

France
Melody from Paris Antiphoner 1681
Harm. Erik Routley 1961

Parata cum te poscerunt

a 4

1. Bo - že___ Ot - če, ___ bud' poch - vá - len, žes nám___ dal
1. Dear Fa - ther, God, _ we rise to say: your name_ be

ten - to dneš - ní - den, v dob - rém___ zdra - ví___ u -
praised for this___ new day. For health_ and strength our

- hlí - da - ti, ó rač___ nám v - še do - bré dá - ti.
pray - ers to lift: grant ev' - ry good___ and_ per - fect gift!

2. Bože Synu, tě žádáme, / at^v tento den to konáme, / co by se Tobě líbilo / a nám spasitelné bylo.

3. Bože Duchu, chraň od zlého, / potěš v zármutku každého, / a když přijde poslední den, / pojmiž nás všech k sobě, Amen.

Jiří Zábojnik 1608–72

2. O God the Son, we pray of you, / may all we plan and say and do / be ever welcome in your sight, / be done to your and our delight.

3. O Spirit God, preserve from fear / all those who fret and sorrow here; / and when the day of days arrives, / with fadeless glory crown our lives.

J. J. Vajda 1969

Philippines
Traditional melody
Elena G. Maquiso 1961
Harm. C.D.

121

1. Fa-ther in hea-ven, grant to your child-ren mer-cy and
2. Je-sus, Re-deem-er, may we re-mem-ber your gra-cious

bles-sing, songs ne-ver ceas-ing, ___ love to u-nite us,___ grace to re-
Pas-sion, your re-sur-rec-tion.___Wor-ship we bring you,___ praise we shall

-deem us,___ Fa-ther in hea-ven,___ Fa-ther our God.
sing you ___ Je-sus, Re-deem-er, ___ Je-sus our Lord.

3. Spirit descending, / whose is the blessing – / strength for the weary, /
help for the needy, / sealed in our sonship / yours be our worship – /
Spirit unending, / Spirit adored.

D. T. Niles 1961

231

122

Germany
Medieval Church Melody
arr. Martin Luther 1524
Harm. C.D.

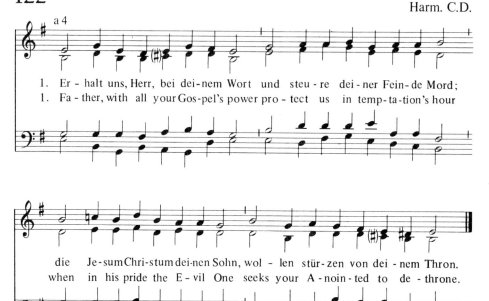

1. Er - halt uns, Herr, bei dei - nem Wort und steu - re dei - ner Fein- de Mord;
1. Fa - ther, with all your Gos-pel's power pro - tect us in temp-ta-tion's hour

die Je-sumChri-stum dei-nen Sohn, wol - len stür-zen von dei - nem Thron.
when in his pride the E - vil One seeks your A - noin - ted to de - throne.

2. Beweis dein Macht, Herr Jesu Christ, / der du Herr aller Herren bist, /
beschirm dein arme Christenheit, / dass sie dich lob in Ewigkeit.

3. Gott, Heilger Geist, du Tröster wert, / gib deim Volk ein'rlei Sinn auf
Erd, steh bei uns in der letzten Not, / g'leit uns ins Leben aus dem Tod.

Martin Luther 1524

2. Our King of glory, Jesus Christ, / power in obedience manifest, /
defend your church in dangerous days / and liberate us for your praise.

3. Spirit by Christ's atonement given / to bring together earth and
heaven / in us, between us, silence strife, / and lead us out of death to
life.

Erik Routley 1973 (last line, Catherine Winkworth)

232

The Church · Its Experience and Faith
Die Kirche · Leben und Glaube
L'Eglise · Expérience et Foi

Ireland
Traditional melody
Harm. Erik Routley 1951

123

Slane

1. Be thou my Vision, O Lord of my heart; all else but nought to me save that thou art; thou my best thought in the day and the night, wak-ing and sleep-ing, thy pre-sence my light.

2. Be thou my wisdom, be thou my true Word; / thou ever with me, and I with thee, Lord; / thou my great Father, and I thy true Son: / thou in me dwelling, and I with thee one.

3. Be thou my breastplate, my sword for the fight: / thou my whole armour, and thou my true might; / thou my soul's shelter, and thou my strong tower: / raise thou me heavenward, great power of my power.

4. Riches I heed not nor man's empty praise, / thou mine inheritance now and always; / thou and thou only the first in my heart; / sovereign of heaven, my treasure thou art.

5. High King of heaven, thou heaven's bright sun, / grant me its joys, after vict'ry is won; / heart of my own heart, whatever befall, / be thou my Vision, O ruler of all.

Mary Byrne 1905, here altered as in BBC Hymn Book 1951

233

124

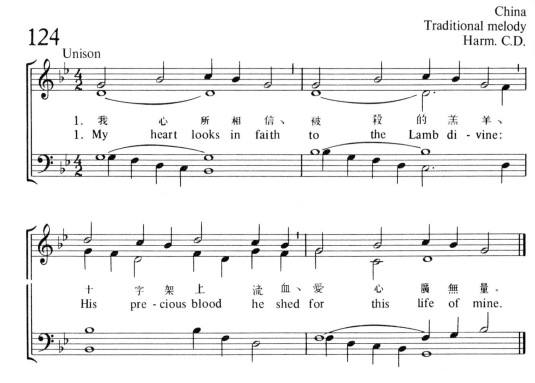

Unison

1. 我　　心　所　相　信、被　　殺　的　羔　羊、
1. My　heart　looks　in　faith　to　the　Lamb di - vine:

十　字　架　上　流　血、愛　心　廣　無　量。
His　pre - cious blood　he shed for　this　life　of　mine.

2. 我心所仰望、聖子主耶穌、罪惡有他救渡、跌倒有他
扶。

3. 我心所敬愛、基督耶穌名、他能使我服務、建立我德
行。

4. 我有信望愛、我有主耶穌、我有全副軍裝、忠勇做門
徒。（阿們。）

T. C. Chao

2. My heart waits in hope / to the Lamb divine: / sure are his promises, / they encompass me.

3. My heart dwells in love / by the Spirit blest; / he heals my sicknesses, / sets my soul at rest.

4. All faith, hope and love / are by Jesus given, / on earth to give us strength / and his peace in heaven.

Frank W. Price 1965

125

Unison

1. おも——い—いずる—も　はず——
　あと——なき—ゆめ—の　あと——
1. Ah what＿ shame I＿ have to＿ bear, for I＿

かしや——ちち—の—み—
をおい——むなし—き—
left my home＿＿ to pur-sue＿ an＿

も—と—を　はな——れきて——
さ—ち—を　たの——しみぬ——
emp-ty dream, spent my＿ life in vain!＿

2　ならわぬわざの　牧　場　守、
　草のいおりの　おきふしに、
　ひとのなさけの　うすごろも、
　うき世の風ぞ　身にはしむ。

3　破れしたもとに　おく露も、
　父のめぐみを　しのばせて、
　まよいの夢も　覚めにけり。
　いざふるさとへ　かえりゆかん。
Sogo Matsumoto

2. In this hut I sleep and wake, / taking care of swine: / no one has pity on me: / loud blows the chilly wind.

3. Tatter'd sleeves are wet with dew / when I think of home. / Waking from my foolish dreams, / to my home I'll go. Esther Hibbard 1962

126

1. Je-su mei-ne Freu - de, mei-nes Her-zens Wei - de,
1. Je-sus, price-less trea - sure, source of pu - rest plea-sure,

Je - su mei-ne Zier, ach,— wie— lang, ach lan - ge
tru-est friend to me, long—my—heart has pant - ed,

ist— dem Her-zen ban - ge, und—ver-langt nach dir.
till— it well nigh faint - ed, thirst-ing af - ter thee.

Got - tes Lamm, mein Bräu - ti - gam, au - ßer dir__ soll
Thine__ I am, O spot - less Lamb, I will suf - fer

mir__ auf__ Er den nichts sonst lie - ber wer - den.
nought to__ hide_____ thee, ask for nought be - side_____ thee.

2. Unter deinem Schirmen / bin ich vor den Stürmen / aller Feinde frei. /
Laß von Ungewittern / rings die Welt erzittern, / mir steht Jesus bei. /
Ob's mit Macht gleich blitzt und kracht, / wenn gleich Sünd und Hölle
schrecken, / Jesus will mich decken.

3. Weicht, ihr Trauergeister; / denn mein Freudenmeister, / Jesus tritt
herein. / Denen, die Gott lieben, / muß auch ihr Betrüben / lauter Freude
sein. / Duld' ich schon hier Spott und Hohn, / dennoch bleibst auch du im
Leide, / Jesus meine Freude.

J. W. Franck 1653

2. In thine arms I rest me; / foes who would molest me / cannot reach
me here. / Though the earth be shaking, / ev'ry heart be quaking, / God
dispels our fear; / sin and hell in conflict fell / with their heaviest storms
assail us: / Jesus will not fail us.

3. Hence, all thoughts of sadness! / for the Lord of gladness, / Jesus,
enters in. / Those who love the Father, / though the storms may gather, /
still have peace within. / Yea, whate'er we here must bear, / still in Thee
liest purest pleasure, / Jesus, priceless treasure!

Catherine Winkworth 1863

127

Germany
Kurt Bossler 1967

1. Und suchst du meine Sünde, flieh ich vor dir_____ zu dir; Ursprung, in den ich münde du fern und nah___ bei mir.

1. Pursued, I find there's only escape from God_____ to God, my freedom and my capture means pardon and___ a rod.

2. Wie ich mich wend und drehe, / geh ich von dir zu dir; / die Ferne und die Nähe / sind aufgehoben hier.

3. Von dir zu dir mein Schreiten, / mein Weg und meine Ruh, / Gericht und Gnade, beides, / bist du, bist immer du.   Schalom Ben-Chorim 1931

2. In restless haste my journey / affords no changing view; / the route on which I hurry / begins and ends with you.

3. My start and destination, / my patron and my guest; / you are my Judge and Saviour; / you are my toil and rest.   Ivor Jones 1972

Germany
Johann Walter 1541
Harm. 1934

128

1. All Mor - gen ist ganz frisch und neu des
1. Each mor - ning with its new - born light pro -

Her - ren Gnad und gro - ße Treu, sie hat kein End den
- claims the Lord of life is great! His faith - ful - ness will

lan - gen Tag, drauf je - der sich ver - las - sen mag.
have no end; to him our songs of praise as - cend.

[vv. 2, 3, 4, 5, 6 overleaf

2. Drum steht der Himmel Lichter voll, / daß man zum Leben sehen soll / und es mög schön geordnet sein, / zu ehren Gott, den Schöpfer dein.

3. So hat der Leib der Augen Licht, / daß er dadurch viel Guts ausricht / und seh auf Gott zu aller Frist / und merk, wie er so gnädig ist.

4. O Gott, du schöner Morgenstern, / gib uns, was wir von dir begehr'n: / zünd deine Lichter in uns an, / laß uns an Gnad kein Mangel han.

5. Treib aus, o Licht, all Finsternis, / behüt uns, Herr, vor Ärgernis, / vor Blindheit und vor aller Schand / und beut' uns Tag und Nacht dein' Hand.

6, Zu wandeln als am lichten Tag, / damit was immer sich zutrag, / wir steh'n im Glauben bis ans End' / und bleiben von dir ungetrennt.

Johannes Zwick (1496–1542)

2. The gift of light that fills the sky / helps us to see and choose our way; / then let us order our affairs / in praise of him who for us cares.

3. Lord, let our eyes, the body's light, / be drawn to what is good and right / and to yourself, the source of life, / our hope in fear, our peace in strife.

4. You, Lord of all creation, are / as brilliant as the morning star; / light in our hearts your holy flame / and make us fit to bear your name.

5. Dispel the darkness from our days / and free us from all bitterness, / from haughty mind and blinded sight, / and lead us forward day and night.

6. To walk as in the light of day, / be steadfast always, come what may, / we turn in faith to you, our Friend, / and pray: sustain us to the end.

Fred Kaan 1972

129

Song 34

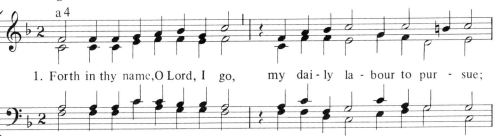

1. Forth in thy name, O Lord, I go, my dai - ly la - bour to pur - sue;

thee, on - ly thee, re - solved _ to know, in all I think or speak or do.

2. The task thy wisdom hath assigned / O let me cheerfully fulfil; / in all my works thy presence find, / and prove thy good and perfect will.

3. Thee may I set at my right hand, / whose eyes my inmost substance see, / and labour on at thy command / and offer all my works to thee.

4. Give me to bear the easy yoke, / and every moment watch and pray, / and still to things eternal look, / and hasten to thy glorious day.

5. For thee delightfully employ / whate'er thy bounteous grace hath given, / and run my course with even joy, / and closely walk with thee to heaven.

Charles Wesley 1749

130

Taiwan
I-to Lòh b. 1936

Unison

(台) 1. 主 祢 交 付 我 工 程、 我 盡 力 在 打 併、
(國) 1. 主 祢 託 代 我 工 作、 勤 勉 不 敢 蹉 跎、
1. 'Light and salt' you called your friends, 'on the hill your ci - ty:

若 是 此 世 間 聲 音、 過 頭 多 攪
無 奈 世 上 太 騷 擾、 令 人 心 煩
let your light shine out for men, skill and peace and

擾 心、 彼 時 我 心 愛 定 定、
意 燥、 那 時 我 心 願 寧 靜、
pi - ty.' But if salt has lost its taste,

集 中 心 神 來 聽、 對 日 日 當
斂 開 注 門 聆 聽、 在 我 每 日
and the light its fu - el, and the ci - ty

做　工　程、　　主　在　聲　示　之　　聲。
工　作　中、　　聽　主　指　來　跟　　從。
shuts　its　gates,　whence　can　come　re - new - al?

台語音

2. 今我於工作中間、驚了只趁世間、雖無嫌境遇艱苦、
　當為生活奔波、懇求天父伸聖手、扶持免受引誘、給
　我於無閒中間、也搃住主平安。

3. 世間生活無單純、容易跌落沈淪、有時明知是不義、
　倘且難得閃避、有時權勢迫我行、辜負我主尊名、願
　我勇敢和清廉、成做世間光塩。

4. 社會辦事愈複雜、人人愈難和合、要緊事情當參詳、
　却無路可商量、願主做仲保概能、使人做事和平、祢
　是世界主人翁、審判地上君王。

國語音

2. 我正服務此世中、恐流俗與世同、雖然不嫌世路艱、
　謀生受苦難免、懇求天父伸聖手、扶持免受引誘、保
　守主民百忙中、時刻與主相通。

3. 世上生活不單純、容易跌倒沈淪、有時明知是不義、
　倘且難得逃避、或許權勢迫我行、辜負我主聖名、願
　我勇敢又清廉、做為世上光塩。

4. 人間事物愈繁雜、人與人難融洽、每逢難事心困擾、
　何處供我商討、懇求我主做橋樑、使人互相體諒、祢
　是救主世無雙、審判世上君王。

John E. Y. Cheng

2. Each in his own place receives / gospel, guidance, duty: / daily bread and daily work, / t'ward the Kingdom's beauty. / Yet the world's distracting scene / mocks our lofty vision. / Life's complexities confuse / conscience and decision.

3. Men dispute and nations fight / each all virtue claiming; / your disciple errs and falls, / false opinion framing. / Judge me, Lord, and plead my cause, / light and truth now send me; / lead me in your righteousness / chasten and befriend me.

Paraphrase by Erik Routley
(Not for simultaneous singing)

131

Hungarian melody 1744
Harm. C.D.

1. Pa - ra - di - csom - nak te szép é - lö fà - ja,
1. There in God's gar - den stands the Tree of wis - dom

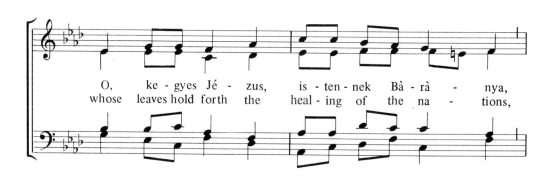

O, ke - gyes Jé - zus, is - ten - nek Bà - rà - nya,
whose leaves hold forth the heal - ing of the na - tions,

te vagy lel-künk-nek i - gaz Meg-vàl-tó - ja, sza - ba-di-tó - ja.
Tree of all know-ledge, Tree of all com-pas - sion, Tree of all beau - ty.

2. Ertünk egyedül szörnyü kint szenvedtél, / megfeszittetvén töviset viseltél, / mi büneinkért véreddel fizettél, / megölettettél.

3. Edes Jézusunk, szenteld meg lelkünket, / hogy megbocsàssuk mi is a bünöket / mindeneknek, kik ellenük vétettek / es elestenek.

4. Adjad, hogy mi is értük könyörögjünk, / téged követvén szivböl esedezzünk, / hogy sok szentekkel tehozzàd mehessünk, / idvezülhessünk.

5. A pàlyafutàst mi is elvégezvén. / lelkünket anjànlhassuk szent kezedbe, / mint megvàltottak mondhassuk nagy szépen / eletünk végében:

6. Hàla légyen a mennybeli Istennek, / ki megvàltója a bünös embernek, / es megszerzöje szent békességünknek, / idvességünknek.

Kiràly Imre von Pécselyi+c 1590-c 1641

2. Its name is Jesus, name that says, 'Our Saviour!' / There on its branches see the scars of suffering; / see where the tendrils of our human selfhood / feed on its life-blood.

3. Thorns not its own are tangled in its foliage; / our greed has starved it; our despite has choked it. / Yet look, it lives! Its grief has not destroyed it, / nor fire consumed it.

4. See how its branches reach to us in welcome; / hear what the voice says, 'Come to me, ye weary! / Give me your sickness, give me all your sorrow. / I will give blessing.'

5. This is my ending; this my resurrection; / into your hands, Lord, I commit my spirit. / This have I searched for; now I can possess it. / This ground is holy!

6. All heaven is singing, 'Thanks to Christ, whose Passion / offers in mercy healing, strength and pardon. / All men and nations, take it, take it freely!' / Amen! My Master!

Erik Routley 1973

132

China
Y. L. Yang 1931
Harm. C.D.

Unison

1. A - rise, —— a - rise my soul—— and praise give to —— the
2. Search thou——the world from end—— to end; where is —— there
3. Thou art——the wea - pon, He—— the hand; all pur - po -

Lord of nights—— and days; forth on the path of
such an - oth - er friend? He leads thee on with
- ses His mind—— has planned. Thy will u - pon His

life—— once more, and God—— the glo - ri - ous—— a - dore.
lov - ing care; ah, fol - low thou Him ev' - ry - where.
al - tar lay, and go—— thou forth with Him—— to - day.

Narayan Vaman Tilak (Marathi) 1862–1919
tr. Nicol Macnicol 1870–1952

The Church · Its Unity and Mission
Die Kirche · Einheit und Mission
L'Eglise · Unité et Mission

Indonesia
Nj. R. Sutisno
Harm. C.D.

133

1. We who bear the hu - man name__ are like flow - ers of the
field;__ with -out sta - tus, with - out fame, tram - pled down and made to
yield, un - pro -tect - ed and ex - posed to the scorch - ing wind that
blows. Let all the world now blos-som as a field!

[vv. 2, 3 overleaf

2. Even Solomon of old, (said our Lord the man of peace) / with his glory and his gold could not match the flowers' grace. / We are weak, but we recall how the mighty men must fall. / Let all the world now blossom as a field.

3. We are people of the field, crowding Asia's city streets. / We are people called to build a community of peace. / We remember as we toil hope is springing from the soil. / Let all the world now blossom as a field.

Masao Takenaka and Fred Kaan 1972

134

England
Orlando Gibbons 1623

1. E - ter - nal Ru - ler___ of the cease - less___ round of circl -ing___ pla -nets sing -ing on their___way; guide of the na - tions___from the night___pro - found in - to the___ glo -ry___

of__ the__per - fect day; rule in our__hearts, that__ we may ev - er
be guid - ed and strength - ened and__ up - held by thee.

2. We are of thee, the children of thy love, / the brothers of thy well-beloved Son; / descend, O Holy Spirit, like a dove / into our hearts, that we may be as one: / as one with thee, to whom we ever tend; / as one with him, our brother and our friend.

3. We would be one in hatred of all wrong, / one in our love of all things sweet and fair, / one with the joy that breaketh into song, / one with the grief that trembleth into prayer, / one in the power that makes thy children free / to follow truth, and thus to follow thee.

4. O clothe us with thy heavenly armour, Lord, / thy trusty shield, thy sword of love divine; / our inspiration be thy constant word; / we ask no victories that are not thine: / give or withhold, let pain or pleasure be; / enough to know that we are serving thee.

J. W. Chadwick 1864

135

Sweden
Sven-Erik Bäck 1970

Unison

1. Se här byg-ges Babels torn sla - var bär dess ste - nar där
1. See them build-ing Ba-bel's tower: slaves the stones are carry-ing: here

up - pe glöm-mer man sin bror (1-3) ky - ri - e - lei - son.
no man cares for bro-ther man:(4-7) Hal - le - lu - ja.

2. Vägen uppåt leder bort / mänskan blir en främling / och bröd lös vid sin broders bord / kyrieleison.

3. Brodersordet har vi glömt / ratat som en byggsten / man slängt i gräset nedanför / kyrieleison.

4. Någon finner den till slut / ser att en förkastad / är hörnsten till Guds berg och hus / halleluja.

5. På vårt eget tungomål / vi en dag hör talas / om broderskapet nerifrån / halleluja.

6. Himmelriket stormar in / över alla gränser / och vinden blåser vart den vill / halleluja.

7. Babels torn skall falla snart / nedanför där växer / Guds vete och hans broderskap / halleluja.

Olov Hartman 1970

2. Far astray that upward road, / man, become a stranger, / goes hungry at his brother's board: / Kyrieleison.

3. 'Brotherhood', forgotten word / down the grassy hillside / rejected from that building lies. / Kyrieleison.

4. Men one day will find it there / and will recognize it / as keystone of God's hill and house. / Hallelujah!

5. Then their cry will rise, and we, / each in his own language / shall hear of brotherhood once more, / Hallelujah!

6. Mighty wind of heaven's rule, / storming every barrier / will blow for ever where it wills, / Hallelujah!

7. So shall Babel come to nought. / Where it stood shall flourish / the harvest of God's brotherhood. / Hallelujah.

Caryl and Ruth Micklem 1972

India
Christopher Coelho 1972
Composed for C.D.

Refrain

Di - vi - ded our path-ways, and hea - vy our guilt;

bur-den'd, un - see - ing, we grope for the one way. Far from our

home, O Fa - ther, we call out - 'Heal us, for - give us:

Fine

bring us to - ge - ther in Je - sus your Son!'

[continued overleaf

Cantor

1. Holy Father, keep those you have gi - ven me true to your Name,
2. Father, may they be one in us as you are in me and I am in you,
3. I have given them the glo - ry that you gave to me,
4. With me in them and you in me may they be so com-plete-ly u - nited,

1. so that they may all __ be one as we are one.
2. so that the world may come to be - lieve it was you who sent __ me.
3. that they may all __ be one as we are one.

4. that the world may know that it was you who sent me,

and that you love them as much as you love me.

Refrain p. 251

John 17 and Christopher Coelho 1972

Unison

1. Help us ac - cept each o - ther as Christ ac - cept - ed us;
2. Teach us, O Lord, your les-sons, as in our dai - ly life

teach us as sis - ter, bro-ther each per - son to em - brace.
we strug - gle to be hu - man and search for hope and faith.

Be pre - sent, Lord a - mong us and bring us to be - lieve
Teach us to care for peo - ple, for all — not just for some,

we are our - selves ac - cept - ed and meant to love and live.
to love them as we find them or as they may be - come.

[vv. 3, 4 overleaf

253

3. Let your acceptance change us, / so that we may be moved / in living situations / to do the truth in love; / to practise your acceptance / until we know by heart / the table of forgiveness / and laughter's healing art.

4. Lord, for today's encounters / with all who are in need, / who hunger for acceptance, / for righteousness and bread, / we need new eyes for seeing, / new hands for holding on: / renew us with your Spirit; / Lord, free us, make us one!

Fred Kaan 1974

tons et nous pro - cla - mons. ___ 2. Ap - pe - lés à for -
sing! let the whole world hear!___ 2. Called to build ___ in

-mer un seul Corps dans un seul Es - prit,_____ nous chan -
love ___ one bo - dy in one___ Spi - rit, let us

-tons et nous pro - cla - mons. ___ 3. Ap - pe - lés à par - ta -
sing; let the whole world hear.___ 3. Called to share in ex - pec -

-ger u - ne seule es - pé - ran - ce dans le
-ta - tion one liv - - ing hope in Je - sus

Christ, nous chan - tons et nous pro - cla - mons._____
Christ, let us sing; let the whole world hear. _____

(E) Erik Routley 1972

255

Hampton Poyle

England
Peter Cutts 1965

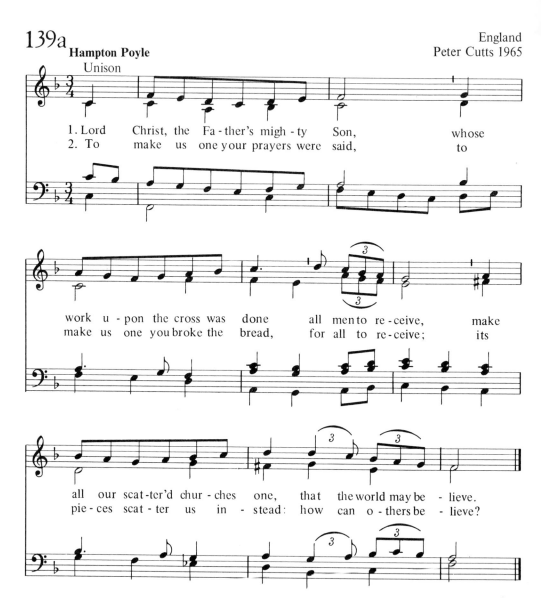

1. Lord Christ, the Fa-ther's migh-ty Son, whose
work u-pon the cross was done all men to re-ceive,
make all our scat-ter'd chur-ches one, that the world may be-lieve.

2. To make us one your prayers were said, to
make us one you broke the bread, for all to re-ceive;
its pie-ces scat-ter us in-stead: how can o-thers be-lieve?

3. Lord Christ, forgive us, make us new! / What our designs could never do / your love can achieve. / Our prayers, our work, we bring to you, / that the world may believe.

4. We will not question or refuse / the way you work, the means you choose, / the pattern you weave; / but reconcile our warring views / that the world may believe.

Brian Wren 1965

256

Jamaica
Doreen Potter 1971
Harm. Erik Routley
Composed for C.D.

139b

Goodwill

a 4

1. Lord Christ, the Father's mighty Son, whose work upon the
2. To make us one your prayers were said, to make us one you

cross was done all men to receive, make
broke the bread, for all to receive; its

all our scat-ter'd churches one, that the world may be-lieve.
pieces scatter us in-stead: how can others be-lieve?

3. Lord Christ, forgive us, make us new! / What our designs could never
do / your love can achieve. / Our prayers, our work, we bring to you, /
that the world may believe.

4. We will not question or refuse / the way you work, the means you
choose, / the pattern you weave; / but reconcile our warring views / that
the world may believe.

Brian Wren 1965

257

U.S.A.
American folk-hymn c. 1815
arr. H. T. Burleigh 1941

140a
McKee
a 4

1. In___ Christ there is no___ East or West, in

him no South or___ North,_____ but___ one___great___ fel - low -

- ship___ of___ love through - out___ the whole___wide earth.

2. In him shall true hearts everywhere / their high communion find, / his service is the golden cord / close-binding all mankind.

3. Join hands, then, brothers of the faith, / whate'er your race may be; / who serves my Father as a son / is surely kin to me.

4. In Christ now meet both East and West, / in him meet South and North, / all Christlike souls are one in him, / throughout the whole wide earth.

John Oxenham 1924

140b

St. Peter

England
A. R. Reinagle 1836

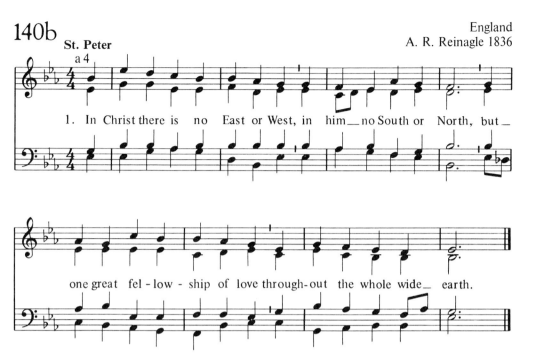

1. In Christ there is no East or West, in him — no South or North, but — one great fel-low-ship of love through-out the whole wide — earth.

2. In him shall true hearts everywhere / their high communion find, / his service is the golden cord / close-binding all mankind.

3. Join hands, then, brothers of the faith, / whate'er your race may be; / who serves my Father as a son / is surely kin to me.

4. In Christ now meet both East and West, / in him meet South and North, / all Christlike souls are one in him, / throughout the whole wide earth.

John Oxenham 1924

141

Jamaica
Doreen Potter 1970

Kingston

1. Ga-thered here__ from ma - ny na - tions, one in wor - ship and in - tent, let us for__ the days that face us all our hopes__ to God pre - sent, __ that our com - mon life may be.__ full of joy__ and__ tru - ly free.

2. May the spring of all our actions / be, O Lord, your love for man; / may your word be seen and spoken / and your will be clearly done. / Help us, who your image bear, / for the good of each to care.

3. Give us grace to match our calling, / faith to overcome the past; / show us how to meet the future, / planning boldly, acting fast. / Let the servant-mind of Christ / in our life be manifest.

4. Now ourselves anew committing / to each other and to you, / Lord, we ask that you will train us / for the truth we have to do; / that the world may soon become / your great city of shalom.

F. H. Kaan 1970

142

Germany
Rolf Schweizer 1967

Unison

1. Herr, du hast dar - um ge - be - tet, daß wir
1. Lord, you of - fered to the Fa - ther prayers that

sol - len ei - nes sein. Hilf du sel - ber uns zur
we might all be one. To that u - ni - ty now

Ein - heit, denn die Kir - che ist ja dein.
lead us: let the Fa - ther's will be done.

[vv. 2, 3, 4, 5 overleaf

2. Dein Reich ist nicht unsre Kirche, / unsre Konfession allein, / nein, dein Reich, Herr, ist viel größer. / Brich mit deinem Reich herein.

3. Laß den Brüdern uns begegnen, / die in andern Kirchen stehn / und sich dort, wie wir es hier tun, / mühen, deinen Weg zu gehn,

4. die mit andern Stimmen loben / deinen großen Namen, Christ, / der für sie, wie auch für uns, Herr, / Name ohnegleichen ist.

5. Laß uns zueinander stehen, / ganz so, wie es dir gefällt, / daß dein Reich in Wahrheit komme, / Herr, in unsre müde Welt.

Otmar Schulz 1967, 1971

2. For our church is not your Kingdom: / this your word may teach us still. / No, your kingdom, Lord, is greater: / reconcile us to your will.

3. Lord, we long to join our brethren / whom our rival laws restrain, / but who study just as we do / Christ's own standards to maintain.

4. Lord, we long to share their worship / who prefer another form, / but whose anthems, just as ours do, / take Christ's glory as their norm.

5. Lord, we long to stand beside them / in fulfilment of your plan, / that by true faith shall your kingdom / bring reality to man.

Ivor Jones 1968, 1971

Germany
Melchior Vulpius 1609
Harm. F. Layriz 1844

143

a 4

1. Christ is the King, O friends, __ re - joice; bro - thers and
2. O mag - ni - fy the Lord, __ and raise an - thems of

sis - ters with one ___ voice make all men know ___ he
joy ___ and ho - ly ___ praise for Christ's brave saints ___ of

is your ___ choice. Al - le - lu - ia! _____
an - cient ___ days. Al - le - lu - ia! _____

Al - le - lu - ia! _____ Al - le - lu - ia!
Al - le - lu - ia! _____ Al - le - lu - ia!

3. O Christian women, Christian men, / all the world over, seek again, /
the Way disciples followed then. / Alleluia!

4. Christ through all ages is the same: / place the same hope in his great
name; / with the same faith his word proclaim. / Alleluia!

5. Let Love's unconquerable might / your scattered companies unite / in
service to the Lord of light. / Alleluia!

6. So shall God's will on earth be done, / new lamps be lit, new tasks
begun, / and his whole Church at last be one. / Alleluia!

Bishop G. K. A. Bell 1883-1958

263

144

Tanzania
Ihandzu-Ilyamba melody

Kiongozi mara ya kwanza. Wote mara ya pili
(Leader, first time;   All, second time)

1. Tu - me - po - ke - a   ne - e - ma;
1. We have from the Lord re - ceived grace,

tu - i - mbe so - te   kwa sha - ngwe.
ex - tol his mer - cies   for ev - er.

Kiongozi mara ya kwanza; Wote mara ya pili
(Leader, first time;   All, second time)

Mu - ngu Ba - ba ka - mpe - le - ka
His Spi - rit he sent to our race,

Ro - ho M - fa - ri - ji wa - ke.
from whom no one us can se - ver.

Refrain after all verses:
Kiongozi   Wote
(Leader)   (All)

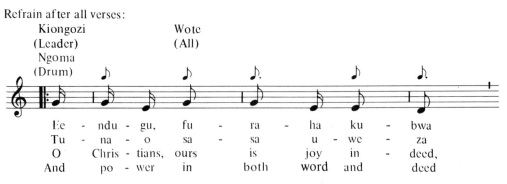

Ee - ndu - gu, fu - ra - ha ku - bwa
Tu - na - o sa - sa u - we - za
O Chris - tians, ours is joy in - deed,
And po - wer in both word and deed

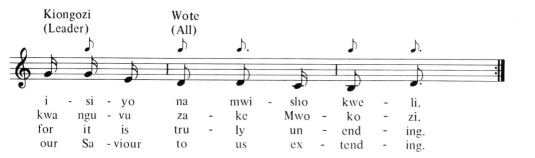

Kiongozi (Leader)   Wote (All)

i - si - yo	na	mwi - sho	kwe - li.
kwa ngu - vu	za - ke	Mwo - ko - zi.
for it is	tru - ly	un - end - ing.
our Sa - viour	to us	ex - tend - ing.

2. Njoo, Roho Mtakatiju, utujaze nguvu zako; / tuende kwa watu wetu, tutangaze neema yako.

3. Ee Roho Mtakatifu, uliye Mwanga wa kweli, / Twapenda kukusukudu, kwandi u pamoja nasi.

4. Ahadi ya Yesu Kristo, hakika imetimizwa; / Twaimarishwa mioyo, tuishuhudie neema.

5. Baba Mungu, naye Mwana, naye Roho Mtakatifu, / Mungu wa Utatu, Mmoja, milele tutakusifu.

Zakarias D. Mzengi

2. O Spirit of truth and of light, dispel deceit and all darkness. / Make truer and clearer our sight to recognize sin's dread starkness.

3. Come Spirit, abide in our heart, transform our weakness to power. / That to others we may impart word of your grace every hour.

4. The promise which Christ gave mankind has been fulfilled to perfection. / He sent us His Spirit; we find in Him sure hope and protection.

5. God Almighty, Father and Son, and Holy Spirit all-knowing, / distinct yet united as One, accept the praise we're bestowing.

Howard S. Olson

265

145

France
Dominique Ombrie

a 4 Refrain

Sei - gneur, ras-sem-ble nous ___ dans la paix ___ de ___ ton a - mour.
U - nite us, Lord, in peace ___ and up - hold ___ us ___ with your love.

Verses Gm   F   Dm

1. Nos fau - tes nous sé - pa - rent, ta grâ - ce nous u - nit; la
1. Our faults di - vide and hin - der; your grace can make us one; we

Cm   Gm   F   Eb6   D maj

joie de ta vic - toi - re é - clai - re no - tre nuit.
won - der at your ris - ing, your light is like the sun.

2. Tu es notre espérance / parmi nos divisions; / plus haut que nos offenses / s'élève ton pardon.

3. Seigneur, vois la misère / des hommes affamés. / Partage à tous nos frères / le pain de l'unité.

4. Heureux le cœur des pauvres / qui cherchent l'unité! / Heureux dans ton royaume / les frères retrouvés.

5. Fais croître en notre attente / l'amour de ta maison; / l'Esprit dans le silence / fait notre communion.

6. Ta croix est la lumière / qui nous a rassemblés; / O joie de notre terre, / tu nous a rachetés.

7. La mort est engloutie, / nous sommes délivrés: / qu'éclate en nous ta vie, / Seigneur ressuscité!

Dominique Ombrie

2. You are our expectation / in loneliness and pain; / your healing and your pardon / are greater than our sin.

3. Lord, look upon the starving / and set the captive free. / Share out among our brothers / the bread of unity.

4. How happy are the people / who strive to be at one, / who learn to live as brothers, / who lay their hatred down.

5. O Lord, whose silent spirit / enlightens and endows, / make us in faith receptive / and help us love your house.

6. Your cross will draw together / the circle of mankind; / in you shall all the people / their true communion find.

7. Death can no longer hurt us, / triumphant is your word. / Let life now grow and blossom, / O Jesus, risen Lord!

Fred Kaan 1972

146a

Unison

1. Ein' fe - ste Burg ist un — ser Gott, ein gu - te Wehr und
1. A safe strong-hold our God__ is still, a trus - ty shield and

Waf - fen. Er hilft uns frei aus al - ler Not, die
wea - pon. He'll help us clear from all__ the ill that

uns jetzt hat be - trof - - fen. Der alt__ bö -
hath us now o'er-ta - - ken. The an - cient prince__

Der alt__ bö -
The an - cient

- - se Feind,
prince of hell,

- se Feind, mit Ernst er es_ jetzt meint, groß Macht und viel_ List
of hell hath ris'n with pur-pose fell; strong mail of craft and power

sein grau - sam Rü - stung ist,   auf Erd ist nicht seins-glei - chen.
he wear - eth in this hour;   on earth is not his fel - low.

2. Mit unsrer Macht ist nichts getan, / wir sind gar bald verloren; / es streit't für uns der rechte Mann, / den Gott selbst hat erkoren. / Fragst du nun, wer der ist? / Er heißt Jesus Christ, / der Herr Zebaoth, und ist kein andrer Gott; / das Feld muß er behalten.

3. Und wenn die Welt voll Teufel wär / und wollt uns gar verschlingen, / so fürchten wir uns nicht so sehr, / es soll uns doch gelingen. / Der Fürst dieser Welt, / wie sauer er sich stellt, / tut er uns doch nichts; / das macht, er ist gericht't; / ein Wörtlein kann ihn fällen.

4. Das Wort sie sollen lassen stahn / und kein Dank dazu haben; / er ist bei uns wohl auf dem Plan, / mit seinem Geist und Gaben. / Nehmen sie uns den Leib, / Gut, Ehre, Kind und Weib, / laß fahren dahin; / sie habens kein Gewinn; / das Reich muß uns doch bleiben.

Martin Luther 1529

2. With force of arms we nothing can, / full soon were we down-ridden; / but for us fights the proper Man, / whom God Himself hath bidden. / Ask ye, who is this same? / Christ Jesus is His name, / of Sabaoth the Lord, / sole God to be adored; / 'tis He must win the battle.

3. And were this world all devils o'er, / and watching to devour us, / we lay it not to heart so sore; / not they can overpower us. / And let the prince of ill / look grim as e'er he will, / he harms us not a whit; / for why? his doom is writ; / a word shall quickly slay him.

4. God's word, for all their craft and force, / one moment will not linger, / but, spite of hell, shall have its course; / 'tis written by His finger. / And, though they take our life, / goods, honour, children, wife, / yet is their profit small; / these things shall vanish all, / the city of God remaineth.

Thomas Carlyle 1831

Alternative version, in Music Edition only

Martin Luther 1529
Harm. J. S. Bach 1739

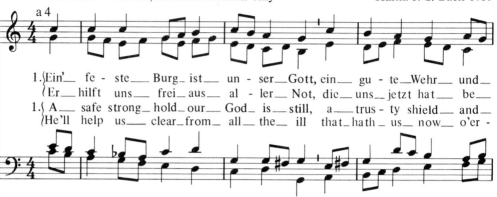

1. {Ein'_ fe - ste_ Burg_ ist_ un - ser_Gott, ein_ gu - te_Wehr_ und
{Er_ hilft uns_ frei_aus_ al - ler_ Not, die_ uns_ jetzt hat_ be-
1. {A _ safe strong_hold_ our_ God_ is _ still, a _ trus - ty shield_ and
{He'll help us_ clear_from_ all_ the_ ill that_hath _ us_ now_ o'er-

Waf - fen.}
trof - fen.} Der_ alt_____ bö - se_ Feind, mit_ Ernst er_ es_ jetzt
wea - pon.} The_ an - cient prince of_ hell hath_ ris'n with_pur - pose
- ta - ken.}

meint, groß Macht_und viel_____ List sein_ grau - sam_ Rü - stung_
fell; strong mail_of craft and_ power he_ wear - eth ___ in this_

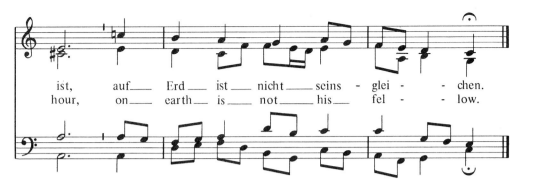

ist, auf___ Erd___ ist___ nicht___ seins - glei - - chen.
hour, on___ earth___ is___ not___ his___ fel - - low.

2. Mit unsrer Macht ist nichts getan, / wir sind gar bald verloren; / es streit't für uns der rechte Mann, / den Gott selbst hat erkoren. / Fragst du nun, wer der ist? / Er heißt Jesus Christ, / der Herr Zebaoth, und ist kein andrer Gott; / das Feld muß er behalten.

3. Und wenn die Welt voll Teufel wär / und wollt uns gar verschlingen, / so fürchten wir uns nicht so sehr, / es soll uns doch gelingen. / Der Fürst dieser Welt, / wie sauer er sich stellt, / tut er uns doch nichts; / das macht, er ist gericht't; / ein Wörtlein kann ihn fällen.

4. Das Wort sie sollen lassen stahn / und kein Dank dazu haben; / er ist bei uns wohl auf dem Plan, / mit seinem Geist und Gaben. / Nehmen sie uns den Leib, / Gut, Ehre, Kind und Weib, / laß fahren dahin; / sie habens kein Gewinn; / das Reich muß uns doch bleiben.

Martin Luther 1529

2. With force of arms we nothing can, / full soon were we down-ridden; / but for us fights the proper Man, / whom God Himself hath bidden. / Ask ye, who is this same? / Christ Jesus is His name, / of Sabaoth the Lord, / sole God to be adored; / 'tis He must win the battle.

3. And were this world all devils o'er, / and watching to devour us, / we lay it not to heart so sore; / not they can overpower us. / And let the prince of ill / look grim as e'er he will, / he harms us not a whit; / for why? his doom is writ; / a word shall quickly slay him.

4. God's word, for all their craft and force, / one moment will not linger, / but, spite of hell, shall have its course; / 'tis written by His finger. / And, though they take our life, / goods, honour, children, wife, / yet is their profit small; / these things shall vanish all, / the city of God remaineth.

Thomas Carlyle 1831

Wales
Thomas John Williams 1890

Ebenezer

1. Lord of light whose name out - shin - eth all the stars and
2. By the toil of low - ly workers in some far out-
3. Grant that knowledge, still in - creas - ing, at thy feet may
4. By the prayers of faith - ful watch-men, nev - er si - lent

suns of space, deign to make us thy co - work - ers
- ly - ing field; by the cour - age where the ra - diance
low - ly kneel; with thy grace our tri - umphs hal - low,
day or night; by the cross of Je - sus bring-ing

in the king - dom of thy grace; use us to ful -
of the cross is still re - vealed; by the vic - to -
with thy cha - ri - ty our zeal; lift the na - tions
peace to men, and heal - ing light; by the love that

- fil thy___ pur - pose in the___ gift of Christ __ thy___ Son:
- ries of___ meek -ness, through re - proach and suf - fering_ won:
from the___ sha - dows to the___ glad - ness of___ the___ sun:
pass - eth___ know-ledge, mak - ing ___ all thy - dren__ one:

1.-4. Fa-ther,_ as in high-est___ hea - ven, so on__ earth thy will_ be done.

Hywel Elvet Lewis 1916

148a

Bohemia
Geistlich Böhmische Brüder 1566

1. Son - ne der Ge - rech - tig - keit, ge - he
1. Sun of Righ - teous - ness, _____ a - rise now, to -

auf zu uns - rer Zeit; brich in dei - ner
- day in our_____ own skies; in your Chur - ch's

Kir - che an, daß die Welt es se - hen kann, er - barm _ dich, Herr.
dawn - ing be that one light by which men see. Have mer - cy, Lord!

2. Weck die tote Christenheit / aus dem Schlaf der Sicherheit; mache
deinen Ruhm bekannt / überall im ganzen Land / Erbarm dich, Herr.

3. Schaue die Zertrennung an, / der kein Mensch sonst wehren kann; /
sammle, grosser Menschenhirt, / alles, was sich hat verirrt. / Erbarm dich,
Herr.

4. Tu der Völker Türen auf, / deines Himmelreiches Lauf / hemme keine
List noch Macht, / schaffe Licht in dunkler Nacht. / Erbarm dich, Herr.

5. Gib den Boten Kraft und Mut, / Glaubenshoffnung, Liebesglut; / laß
viel Früchte deiner Gnad / folgen ihrer Tränensaat. / Erbarm dich, Herr.

6. Laß uns deine Herrlichkeit / ferner sehn in dieser Zeit / und mit
unsrer kleinen Kraft / üben gute Ritterschaft. / Erbarm dich, Herr.

148b

Bohemia
Geistlich Böhmische Brüder 1531
Harm. C.D.

Freuen wir uns
a 4

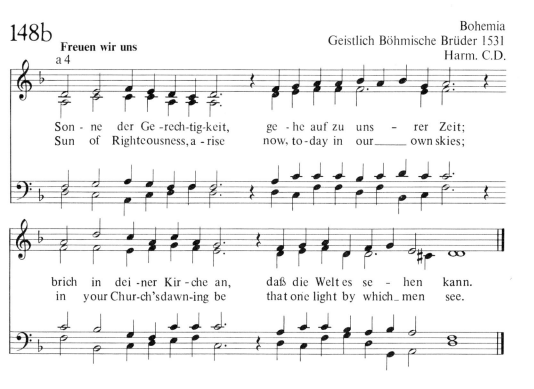

Son - ne der Ge -rech-tig-keit,   ge - he auf zu uns – rer Zeit;
Sun of Righteousness, a - rise   now, to-day in our___ own skies;

brich in dei -ner Kir - che an,   daß die Welt es se - hen kann.
in your Chur-ch's dawn-ing be   that one light by which_ men see.

7. Kraft, Lob, Ehr und Herrlichkeit / sei dem Höchsten allezeit, / der, wie
er ist drei in ein, / uns in ihm läßt eines sein. / Erbarm dich, Herr.

vv. 1, 6 Christian David 1690-1751

vv. 2, 4, 5 Christian Gottlob Barth 1799-1862

vv. 3, 7 Christian Nehring 1671-1725

arranged by Otto Riethmüller 1889–1938

2. Wake dead Christianity, sleeping / in complacency; / may it listen to
you, Lord,/ turn again and trust your Word. / Have mercy, Lord. /

3. See your Church by troubles rent / men were helpless to prevent; /
gather, Shepherd of us all, / those who stumble, stray and fall. / Have
mercy, Lord.

4. Open wide your people's doors; / may no guile, no earthly powers, /
do your Kingdom harsh despite. / Lord, create in darkness light. / Have
mercy, Lord.

5. Give your servants from above / faith and courage, hope and love; /
let rich harvests there be grown / where they have in ,sorrow sown. /
Have mercy, Lord.

6. Let us see your glory now / as about the world we go; / with our little
strength increase / whatsoever makes for peace. / Have mercy, Lord.

7. Every honour, glory, praise, / shall the Highest have always; / so that
in the Three–in–One / we ourselves shall be at one.

F. Pratt Green 1971

149

Purpose

England
Martin Shaw 1931

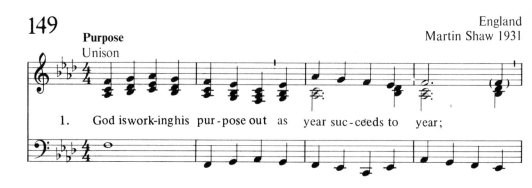

1. God is work-ing his pur-pose out as year suc-ceeds to year;

God is work-ing his pur-pose out and the time is draw-ing near.

Near-er and near-er draws the time, the time that shall sure-ly

be, when the earth shall be filled with the glo-ry of God as the

wa - ters co -ver the   sea.   sea.

2. What can we do to work God's work, / to prosper and increase / the brotherhood of all mankind, / the reign of the Prince of Peace? / What can we do to hasten the time, / the time that shall surely be, / when the earth shall be filled with the glory of God / as the waters cover the sea.

3. March we forth in the strength of God / with the banner of Christ unfurled, / that the light of the glorious Gospel of truth / may shine throughout the world; / fight we the fight with sorrow and sin / to set their captives free, / that the earth shall be filled with the glory of God / as the waters cover the sea.

A. C. Ainger 1894

Germany
P. E. Ruppel 1965

150

Semichorus: 2 voices in Canon

Gleich wie mich mein Va - ter ge -
As my heavenly Fa - ther has

- sandt hat, so sen - de ich euch. — 1.+2. { Er hat mich ge - sandt zu pre-
Und ich sen - de euch zu pre-

sent me, so I am send-ing you. — 1.+2. { He has sent — me to tell—
I am send-ing you to tell—

Fine

2nd time D.C.

- di - gen den Ge - fan - ge - nen, daß sie los sein— sol - len.
- di - gen den Zer - schla - ge - nen, daß sie frei sein— sol - len.
— those in pri - son that their cap - ti - vi - ty is— o - ver.
— the op - press'd and poor that their night of sor - row is end - ed.

St. John 20 : 21
St. Luke 4 : 18
Isaiah 61 : 1

The Holy Communion and the Last Things
Das Heilige Abendmahl und die letzten Dinge
La Sainte-Cêne et les Choses Dernières

Germany
Johann Crüger 1653
Harm. C.D.

151

1. Das sollt ihr, Je - su Jün - ger, nie ver - ges - sen:
1. Let all who share one bread and cup re - mem - ber

wir sind, die wir von ei - nem Bro - te es - sen, aus ei - nem
the one - ness of that host of count-less num - ber of those who

Kel - che trin - ken, al - le Brü - der und Je - su Glie - der.
are, as chil-dren of one Fa - ther, part of each o - ther.

2. Wenn wir wie Brüder beiander wohnten, / Gebeugte stärkten und der Schwachen schonten, / dann würden wir den letzten heilgen Willen / des Herrn erfüllen.

3. Ach dazu müsse seine Lieb uns dringen! / Du wolltest, Herr, dies grosse Werk vollbringen, / daß unter einem Hirten eine Herde / aus allen werde.
Based on a hymn by J. A. Cramer 1723-88

[English vv. 2, 3 overleaf

2. If only we would learn to live as brothers, / put faith to practice, truly care for others, / then we would do the will of Him who sends us, / whose love attends us.

3. Use for yourself our highest and profoundest, / so that, O Lord, with all men who surround us, / we may enjoy a world in Christ united, / so long awaited.

Fred Kaan 1972

France
Carol melody
Harm. Ralph Vaughan Williams 1906

152 Picardy

1. Let all mor-tal flesh keep — si - lence and with fear and trem - bling— stand; pon-der noth - ing earth - ly___ mind - ed, for with bless-ing in his___ hand Christ our Lord to earth des -

-cend - - - eth, our full ho-mage to de - mand.

2. King of kings, yet born of Mary, / as of old on earth he stood, / Lord of lords, in human vesture / – in the Body and the Blood – / he will give to all the faithful / his own Self for heavenly food.

3. Rank on rank the host of heaven / spreads its vanguard on the way, / as the Light of light descendeth / from the realms of endless day, / that the powers of hell may vanish / as the darkness clears away.

4. At his feet the six-winged seraph: / cherubim with sleepless eyes, / veil their faces to the Presence, / as with ceaseless voice they cry, / 'Alleluia, Alleluia, / Alleluia, Lord most high.'

G. Moultrie, from the Greek Liturgy of St James

153

Unison

1. Let us break bread to-geth-er on our knees; let us

Refrain

break bread to-geth-er on our knees: When I fall on my knees, with my

face to the ris-ing sun, O Lord, have mer-cy on me!

2. Let us drink wine together on our knees; / let us drink wine together
on our knees: / when I fall on my knees, / with my face to the rising
sun, / O Lord, have mercy on me.

3. Let us praise God together on our knees; / let us praise God together
on our knees: / when I fall on my knees, / with my face to the rising
sun, / O Lord, have mercy on me.

Negro Spiritual, early 19th century

154 **Sursum corda**

Unison

1. Come, ri - sen Lord, and deign to be our guest; nay, let us be thy guests, the feast is thine: thy - self at thine own board make ma - ni - fest in this our sa - cra - ment of bread and wine.

2. We meet, as in that upper room they met; / thou at the Table blessing yet dost stand: / 'This is my Body', so thou givest yet: / faith still receives the cup as from thy hand.

3. One body we, one body who partake, / one church united in communion blest; / one name we bear, one bread of life we break, / with all thy saints in earth and saints at rest.

4. One with each other, Lord, for one in thee, / who art one Saviour and one living head; / then open thou our eyes, that we may see; / be known to us in breaking of the bread.

G. W. Briggs 1875–1959

155 **Bayhead**

U.S.A.
Lee Hastings Bristol, Jr. 1971

Unison

1. As the dis - ci - ples when thy Son had left them, ___

___ met in a love - feast joy - ful - ly con - vers - ing, ___

___ all the stor'd mem - 'ry of the Lord's last Sup - per, ___

___ fond - ly re - hears - ing; ___ so may we here who

ga - ther now in friend - ship,_____ seek for the spi - rit
of those ear - lier chur - ches;_____ wel - com - ing him who
stands and for an en - trance_____ pa - tient- ly search - es.

2. As when their converse closed and supper ended, / taking the bread
and wine, they made thanksgiving, / breaking and blessing thus to have
communion / with Christ the living; / so may we here, a company of
brothers, / make this our lovefeast and commemoration / that in his
Spirit we may have more worthy / participation.

3. And as they prayed and sang to thee rejoicing, / ere in the nightfall
they embraced and parted, / in their hearts singing as they journeyed
homeward, / brave and truehearted; / so may we here, like grain that
once was scattered, / over the hillside, now one bread united, / led by the
Spirit, do thy work rejoicing, / lamps fill'd and lighted.

Percy Dearmer 1931

India
Urdu melody
Harm. F. B. Westbrook 1969

156

Yisu ne kaha
Unison

1. Je - sus the Lord said: 'I am the Bread, the Bread of Life for man-kind am I, the Bread of Life for man - kind am I, the Bread of Life for man - kind am I.' Je - sus the Lord said: 'I am the Bread, the Bread of Life for man - kind am I.'

One tone higher in Melody Edition

2. Jesus the Lord said: 'I am the Door, / the Way and the Door for the poor am I.'

3. Jesus the Lord said: 'I am the Light, / the one true Light of the world am I.'

4. Jesus the Lord said: 'I am the Shepherd, / the one Good Shepherd of the sheep am I.'

5. Jesus the Lord said: 'I am the Life, / the Resurrection and the Life am I.'

Dermott Monahan 1962

157a

Sheng en (God's grace)

China
Su Yin-Lan 1934
Harm. B.B.C. Hymn Book 1951

1. The bread of life for all men bro - ken! He drank the cup on Gol - go' - tha. His grace we trust, and spread with rev' - rence this ho - ly feast, and this re - mem - ber.

2. With godly fear we seek thy presence; / our hearts are sad, people distressed. / Thy holy face is stained with bitter tears, / our human pain still bearest thou with us.

3. O Lord we pray, come thou among us, / lighten our eyes, brightly appear. / Immanuel, heaven's joy unending, / our life with thine for ever blending.

W. R. O. Taylor

1. 救世之身、為眾生擘開、在骷髏地、痛飲苦杯；蒙恩
   信眾、奉命常紀念、敬設聖筵、追憶當年。

2. 吾眾今朝、虔誠來入覲、國難民愁、遍心創痕；仰瞻
   聖容、看血淚千行、人間苦痛、主仍擔當。

3. 懇求臨格、在我們中間、開我心目、昭現妙身；以馬
   內利、天福永無邊、與主合一、同享永生。阿們。

Timothy Lew

287

157b

Unison

1. The bread of life for all men bro-ken! He drank the cup on Gol-go-tha. His grace we trust, and spread with rev'-rence this ho-ly feast, and this re-mem-ber.

2. With godly fear we seek thy presence; / our hearts are sad, people distressed. / Thy holy face is stained with bitter tears, / our human pain still bearest thou with us.

3. O Lord we pray, come thou among us, / lighten our eyes, brightly appear. / Immanuel, heaven's joy unending, / our life with thine for ever blending.

W. R. O. Taylor

1. 救世之身、為眾生擘開、在骷髏地、痛飲苦杯；蒙恩信眾、奉命常紀念、敬設聖筵、追憶當年。

2. 吾眾今朝、虔誠來入覲、國難民愁、遍心創痕；仰瞻聖容、看血淚千行、人間苦痛、主仍擔當。

3. 懇求臨格、在我們中間、開我心目、昭現妙身；以馬內利、天福永無邊、與主合一、同享永生。阿們。

Timothy Lew

158

Canada
Stanley L. Osborne 1971

Masson

Unison

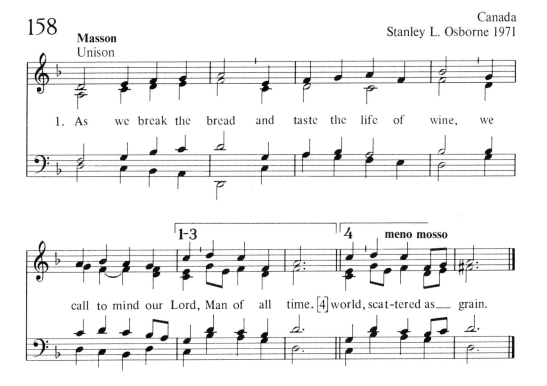

1. As we break the bread and taste the life of wine, we
call to mind our Lord, Man of all time. [4] world, scat-tered as__ grain.

1-3 **4** meno mosso

2. Grain is sown to die; it rises from the dead, / becomes through human toil our common bread.

3. Pass from hand to hand the living love of Christ! / Machine and man provide bread for this feast.

4. Having shared the bread that dies to rise again, / we rise to serve the world, scattered as grain.

Fred Kaan 1968

289

159

1. Herr, du bist an vie - len Ti - schen ein - ge - la - den und zu Gast.
1. Lord, you are at ma - ny ta - bles an in - vi - ted, ho-noured guest.

Und auch bei de - nen, die sich selbst ge-nü - gen, wird kei - ner dir zur
E - ven of those, Lord, who are self-suf-fi - cient you let none bear you

Last. Tei - le mit uns___ das Mahl, tei - le mit uns___
down. Come, share the meal___ with us, come, share the meal___

___ das Mahl, ver - bin - de, die lieb - los sich tren - nen.
___ with us, u - nite those who part with- out lov - ing.

2. Herr, du bist an vielen Tischen / eingeladen und zu Gast. / Sprichst auch mit denen, / die sonst nichts erwarten / als neuer Tage Last. / Teile mit uns das Mahl, / teile mit uns das Mahl, / gib Glanz in die Augen der Müden.

3. Herr, du bist an vielen Tischen / eingeladen und zu Gast. / Kommst auch zu Menschen, / die sich dir versagen. / Frommtun ist dir verhaßt. / Teile mit uns das Mahl, / teile mit uns das Mahl, / daß wir deinem Angebot trauen.

4. Herr, du bist an vielen Tischen / eingeladen und zu Gast. / Sorgst dann als Gastherr, / daß wir uns ertragen, / einer des andern Last. / Teile mit uns das Mahl, / teile mit uns das Mahl, / jetzt hier und an all unsren Tischen.

Dieter Trautwein 1967

2. Lord, you are at many tables / an invited, honoured guest. / You also speak, Lord, / to those who see nothing / except tomorrow's cares. / Come, share the meal with us, / come, share the meal with us, / give light to the eyes of the weary.

3. Lord, you are at many tables / an invited, honoured guest. / You come to people / who do without you. / False piety you hate. / Come, share the meal with us, / come, share the meal with us, / then, Lord, we shall trust what you offer.

4. Lord, you are at many tables / an invited, honoured guest. / But as our Host, Lord, / you make sure we carry / each other's load of cares. / Come, share the meal with us, / come, share the meal with us, / here, now, and at each of our tables.

F. Pratt Green 1973

160

Deus tuorum militum

France
Grenoble Antiphoner 1746

Unison

1. Now let us from this ta - ble rise re - newed in
2. With minds a - lert, up - held by grace, to spread the

bo - dy, mind and soul; with Christ we die and
Word in speech and deed, we fol - low in the

live a - gain, his self - less love has made us whole.
steps of Christ, at one with man in hope and need.

In Melody Edition, one tone lower

3. To fill each human house with love, / it is the sacrament of care; / the
work that Christ began to do / we humbly pledge ourselves to share.

4. Then give us courage, Father God, / to choose again the pilgrim
way, / and help us to accept with joy / the challenge of tomorrow's day.

Fred Kaan 1968

161 **Les Commandements de Dieu**

1. Fa - ther, we thank thee who hast plant - ed Thy ho - ly name with- in our hearts. Know - ledge and faith and life im - mor - tal Je - sus thy Son to us im - parts.

One tone lower in Melody Edition

2. Thou, Lord, didst make all for thy pleasure, / didst give man food for all his days, / giving in Christ the bread eternal; / thine is the power, be thine the praise.

3. Watch o'er thy Church, O Lord, in mercy, / save it from evil, guard it still, / perfect it in thy love, unite it, / cleansed and conformed unto thy will.

4. As grain, once scattered on the hillsides, / was in the broken bread made one, / so from all lands thy Church be gathered / into thy kingdom by thy Son.

F. Bland Tucker 1940

Sweden
Sven-Erik Bäck 1959

Unison

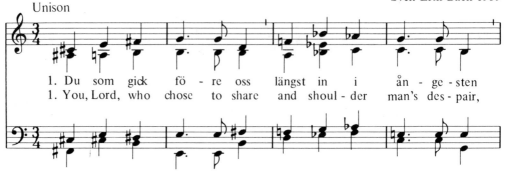

1. Du som gick fö - re oss längst in i ån - ge - sten
1. You, Lord, who chose to share and shoul - der man's des - pair,

hjälp oss att fin - na dig Her - re, i mör - - kret.
be where your peo - ple are in fear and dark - ness.

2. Du som bar all vår skuld in i förlåtelsen / du är vårt hjärtas fred Jesus, för evigt.

3. Du som med livets bröd går genom tid och rum / giv oss för varje dag Kristus, det brödet.

4. Du som går före oss ut i en trasig värld / sänd oss med fred och bröd Herr, i världen.

Olov Hartmann 1968

2. Lord, you who went before, counting our sins no more, / peace to our hearts restore; be with us always.

3. You, who with living bread fill the earth far and wide, / each day this bread provide, Christ, at our table.

4. You, Lord, who went ahead into a world of dread, / send us with peace and bread to all your people.

Fred Kaan 1972

163a

Unison

1. „Wa - chet auf", ruft uns die Stim - me, der Wäch - ter sehr hoch
1. 'Sleep- ers wake!' with ti - dings thrill - ing, the watch-men all the

auf der Zin - ne, „wach auf, du Stadt Je - ru - sa - lem."
air are fill - ing, 'a - rise, Je - ru - sa - lem, a - rise!'

Mit - ter - nacht heißt die - se Stun - de, sie ru - fen uns mit
Mid - night strikes! No more de - lay - ing, 'the hour has come', we

[continued overleaf

hel - lem Mun - de: „Wo seid ihr klu-gen Jung-frau - en?" Wohl -
hear them say - ing, 'where are you all, you vir-gins wise?' The

- auf, der Bräut-gam kommt, steht auf, die Lam-pen nehmt! Hal-le-lu - ja!
Bride-groom comes in sight; raise high your torch-es bright. Al-le-lu - ia!

Macht euch be - reit zu der Hoch - zeit; ihr müs-set ihm ent-ge-gen-gehn!
The wed-ding song swells loud and strong: go forth and join the fes - tal throng.

2. Zion hört die Wächter singen, / das Herz tut ihr vor Freuden springen, / sie wachet und steht eilend auf. / Ihr Freund kommt vom Himmel prächtig, / von Gnaden stark, von Wahrheit mächtig, / ihr Licht wird hell, ihr Stern geht auf. / Nun komm, du werte Kron, / Herr Jesu, Gottes Sohn! / Hosianna! / Wir folgen all zum Freudensaal, / und halten mit das Abendmahl.

3. Gloria sei dir gesungen, / mit Menschen und mit Engelzungen, / mit Harfen und mit Zimbeln schön. / Von zwölf Perlen sind die Tore / an deiner Stadt, wir steh'n im Chore / der Engel hoch um deinen Thron. / Kein Aug hat je gespürt, / kein Ohr hat mehr gehört / solche Freude. / Des jauchzen wir und singen dir / das Halleluja für und für.

Philipp Nicolai 1599

2. Sion hears the watchmen shouting, / her heart leaps up with joy undoubting, / she stands and waits with eager eyes. / See her Friend from heav'n descending, / adorned with truth and grace unending! / Her light burns clear, her star doth rise. / Now come, thou precious crown, / Lord Jesus, God's own Son, / Hosanna! / Let us prepare to follow there, / where in thy supper we may share.

3. Every soul in Thee rejoices; / from men and from angelic voices / be glory given to Thee alone! / Now the gates of pearl receive us, / thy presence never more shall leave us, / we stand with Angels round Thy throne. / Earth cannot give below / the bliss Thou dost bestow. / Alleluia! / Grant us to raise to length of days / the triumph-chorus of Thy praise.

F. C. Burkitt 1906

163b

Alternative version, in Music Edition only

1. „Wa - chet auf", ruft uns __ die __ Stim - - me, der __
Mit - ter - nacht heißt die - se __ Stun - - de, sie __
1. 'Sleep - ers wake!' with ti - dings __ thril - - ling, the __
Mid - night strikes! No more __ de - lay - - ing, 'the __

Wäch - ter __ sehr __ hoch auf __ der __ Zin - - - ne, „wach __
ru - fen __ uns __ mit hel - lem __ Mun - - - de: „Wo __
watch - men __ all __ the air __ are __ fil - - - ling, 'a -
hour __ has __ come,' we hear __ them __ say - - - ing, 'where __

1st time | 2nd time

auf, __ du __ Stadt __ Je - ru - sa - lem."
seid __ ihr __ klu - gen   Jung - frau - en?"   Wohl -
- rise, __ Je - ru - sa - lem, __ a - rise!'
are __ you __ all, __ you   vir - gins wise?'   The

298

-auf, der___ Bräut-gam___ kommt, steht___ auf,___ die___ Lam - pen___
Bride - groom ___ comes in ___ sight; raise ___ high___ your___ torch - es___

nehmt! Hal - le - lu - ja! Macht euch___ be - reit zu___
bright. Al - le - lu - ia! The wed - ding___ song swells___

der___ Hoch - zeit; ihr___ müs - set___ ihm ___ ent - ge - gen - gehn!
loud___ and strong: go___ forth___ and ___ join___ the fes - tal throng.

2. Zion hört die Wächter singen, / das Herz tut ihr vor Freuden springen, / sie wachet und steht eilend auf. / Ihr Freund kommt vom Himmel prächtig, / von Gnaden stark, von Wahrheit mächtig, / ihr Licht wird hell, ihr Stern geht auf. / Nun komm, du werte Kron, / Herr Jesu, Gottes Sohn! / Hosianna! / Wir folgen all zum Freudensaal, / und halten mit das Abendmahl.

[v. 3 overleaf

3. Gloria sei dir gesungen, / mit Menschen und mit Engelzungen, / mit Harfen und mit Zimbeln schön. / Von zwölf Perlen sind die Tore / an deiner Stadt, wir steh'n im Chore / der Engel hoch um deinen Thron. / Kein Aug hat je gespürt, / kein Ohr hat mehr gehört / solche Freude. / Des jauchzen wir und singen dir / das Halleluja für und für.

Philipp Nicolai 1599

2. Sion hears the watchmen shouting, / her heart leaps up with joy undoubting, / she stands and waits with eager eyes. / See her Friend from heav'n descending, / adorned with truth and grace unending! / Her light burns clear, her star doth rise. / Now come, thou precious crown, / Lord Jesus, God's own Son, / Hosanna! / Let us prepare to follow there, / where in thy supper we may share.

3. Every soul in Thee rejoices; / from men and from angelic voices / be glory given to Thee alone! / Now the gates of pearl receive us, / thy presence never more shall leave us, / we stand with Angels round Thy throne. / Earth cannot give below / the bliss Thou dost bestow. / Alleluia! / Grant us to raise to length of days / the triumph-chorus of Thy praise.

F. C. Burkitt 1906

164

Sheen

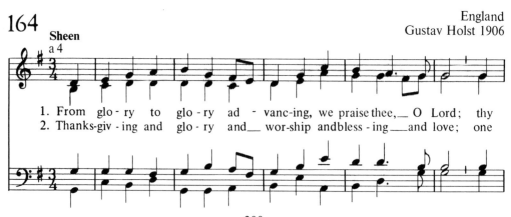

1. From glo-ry to glo-ry ad - vanc-ing, we praise thee,__ O Lord; thy
2. Thanks-giv-ing and glo-ry and__ wor-ship and bless - ing__ and love; one

name with the Fa - ther __ and Spi - rit be ev - er a - dored. From
heart and one song __ have __ the saints up - on earth and a - bove. Ev -

strength un - to strength we go for - ward on Si - on's high - way,
- more __ O Lord, to thy ser - vants thy pre - sence be nigh;

to ap- pear be - fore God in the __ ci - ty of __ in - fi - nite day.
ev - er fit us by ser - vice on __ earth for thy __ ser - vice on high.

(E) C. W. Humphreys 1906 from the Greek Liturgy of St James 4th century

301

165

France
Claude Rozier

1. Puis - sance ___ et gloi - re de ___ l'Es -prit: heu-
1. Your power ___ and glo - ry, Ho - ly Ghost, as -

- reux ___ les vrais mar - tyrs! ___ La chair ___ dont Dieu les
- sure ___ the mar - tyrs' prize; ___ their flesh, ___ re - sem - bling

a ___ pé - tris en lui ___ pour - ra ___ sur - gir. ___
Christ ___ the most in him, ___ re - new'd ___ can rise. ___

2. Pareil aux grains qui sont broyés / pour être notre pain, / leur Corps se joint au Corps brisé / qui s'offre par nos mains.

3. Leur sang se mêle au Sang sauveur / qui lave nos péchés, / ils sont l'amour du même Cœur / qui nous a tant aimés.

4. Heureux qui donne sans compter / jusqu' à sa propre chair! / Il trouve en Dieu sa liberté, / visage découvert.

5. La chair es vaine sans l'Esprit / et cendre dans la mort. / Par votre Croix, Seigneur, survit / la gloire de nos corps.

6. Dans vos martyrs, c'est vous qu'on tue, / mais vous qu'on glorifie; / car votre Eglise en eux salue / la force de l'Esprit.

7. Le grain survit dans la moisson, / au jour de votre Jour. / La vie, la mort n'ont plus de nom / au règne de l'Amour.

Claude Rozier

2. Like wheat grain, crushed to make our bread, / and kneaded for our good, / their broken bodies join their Head, / our sacramental food.

3. Their blood is shed with him and part / of him, for sin's amends; / their love is fed from Jesus' heart, / who died to save his friends.

4. How blest are they who count no cost, / when flesh and courage fail! / They find in God the life they lost, / see him without a veil.

5. Apart from Spirit, flesh is vain, / it turns to dust in death. / Your way, O Lord, through cross and pain / is Spirit's life and health.

6. Each martyr killed is Jesus slain, / and, Lord, your glorious hour; / your Church discerns in all their pain / the Spirit's conquering power.

7. Their life and death are but the loam / that feeds, in Jesus' way, / the seeds that live when harvest's home / on Love's triumphant Day.

Emily Chisholm 1951

Liturgical Material · Liturgische Gesänge
Matériel Liturgique

166

Byzantine 15th century
tr. and arr. D. E. Conomos

"Α - ξι - ον ἐ - στὶν ὡς ἀ - λη - θῶς μα - κα - ρί - ζειν σε
A - xi - on e - stin os a - li - thos ma - ka - ri - zin se

τὴν Θε - ο - τό - κον, τὴν ἀ - ει - μα - κά - ρι - στον, καὶ
tin The - o - to - kon, tin a - i - ma - ka - ri - ston, ke

πα - να μώ - μη - τον, καὶ Μη - τέ - ρα τοῦ Θε - οῦ ἡ -
pa - na - mo - mi - ton, ke Mi - te - ra tou The - ou i -

- μῶν, Τὴν Τι - μι - ω - τέ - ραν τῶν Χε - ρου - βὶμ καὶ ἐν -
- mon. Tin Ti - mi - o - te - ran ton khe - rou - vim ke en -

- δο - ξο - τέ - ραν ἀ - συγ - κρί - τως τῶν Σε - ρα - φείμ,
- tho - xo - te - ran a - sing - kri - tos ton se - ra - fim,

τὴν ἀ - δι - α - φθό - ρως, Θε - ὸν Λό - γον τε - κοῦ - σαν, τὴν ὄν -
tin a - di - af - tho - ros, The - on Lo - gon te - kous - san, tin on -

- τως Θε - ο - τό - κον, σὲ με - γα - λύ - νο - μεν.
- tos The - o - to - kon, se me - ga - li - no - men.

304

It is very meet to bless Thee who didst bring forth God, ever blessed and most spotless and the Mother of our God. More honourable than the Cherubim, and glorious incomparably more than the Seraphim, thou who inviolate didst bring forth God the Word, and art indeed Mother of God, thee do we magnify.

(English paraphrase, not to be sung)

Il est digne et juste en vérité de te bénir, Mère de Dieu, toujours bienheureuse et toute immaculée et la Mère de notre Dieu, plus vénérable que les Chérubins et plus glorieuse que les Séraphins, toi qui sans perdre ton intégrité as conçu Dieu le Verbe, tu es vraiment la Mère de Dieu, nous chantons ta gloire.

(Paraphrase française, à ne pas chanter)

167 a

Kievan melody

305

167b

It is ve - ry meet to bless thee who didst bring forth

God, ev - er bless - ed and most spot - less and the Moth - er

of our God. More hon - our - a - ble than the che - ru - bim,

and glo - rious in - com - pa - ra - bly more than the se - ra -

- phim, thou who in - vi - o - late didst bring for th God the Word,

and art in - deed Moth - er of God, thee do we mag - ni - fy.

168

Traditional Serbian melody

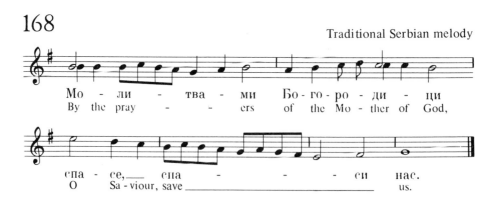

Мо - ли - тва - ми Бо - го - ро - ди - ци
By the pray - - ers of the Mo - ther of God,

спа - се,___ спа - - - си нас.
O Sa - viour, save _____ us.

169

Traditional Serbian melody

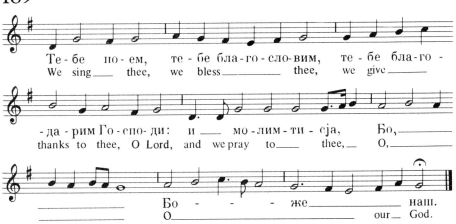

Те - бе по - ем, те - бе бла - го - сло-вим, те - бе бла - го -
We sing___ thee, we bless___ thee, we give___

- да - рим Го - спо- ди: и ___ мо-лим-ти - ся, Бо, _____
thanks to thee, O Lord, and we pray to___ thee, ___ O, _____

_____ Бо - - же _____ наш.
_____ О - - - our___ God.

170

Traditional Roumanian melody

Pre Ti - ne_____ Te_____ lā - u - dăm,

pre Ti - ne_____ bi - ne_____ Te_____

cu - - vîn - tăm. Ti - e îţi mul - ţu -

- mim, _____ Doam - ne şi ne ru - găm___ Ti - e,

Dum - ne - ze - u - lui_____ no - - stru.

We sing Thee, we bless Thee, we give thanks to Thee, O Lord, and we
pray to Thee, our God.

(English paraphrase, not to be sung)

307

171

Πᾶ - - σα πνο - ή_____ αἰ - νε - σά - - τω
Pas - - sa pno - i_____ e - nes - sa - - to

τὸν___ Κύ - - - ρι - - - ον. Αἰ - νεῖ -
ton___ ki - - - ri - - - on. E - ni -

- τε τόν Κύ - - - - ρι - - -
- te ton ki - - - - ri - - -

- ον, ___ 'Αλ - - λη - λού - - ï - α
- on, ___ al - - li - lou - - i - a.

Let everything that hath breath praise the Lord. Praise the Lord. Alleluia.

(English paraphrase, not to be sung)

172

Χρι - στός ἀ - νέ - στη ἐκ νε - κρῶν, θα - νά - - τω
Chri - stos a - ne - sti ek ne - kron, tha - na - - to

θά - να - τον πα - τή - σας, καί τοῖς ἐν τοῖς
tha - na - ton pa - ti - sas, ke tis en tis

μνή - μα - σι ζω - ήν χα - ρι - σά - με - νος.
mni - ma - si zo - in ha - ri - sa - me - nos.

Christ is risen from the dead, trampling down death by death, and to those in the tombs hath he given life.

English paraphrase, not to be sung

173

Byzantine 15th century
tr. and arr. D. E. Conomos

Κύ - ρι - ε ἐ - λέ - η - σον, Κύ - ρι - ε
Ky - ri - e e - le - i - son, Ky - ri - e

ἐ - λέ - η - σον,
e - le - i - son,

Κύ - ρι - ε ἐ - λέ - η - σον.
Ky - ri - e e - le - i - son.

309

174

Ца-рю не-бес-ный у-те-ши-те-лю ду-ше и-сти-ный
O heav-en-ly King, the Com-for-ter Spi-rit of truth

и-же вез-де_____ сый и вся ис-пол-ня-яй
who fill-est all_____ things, who art in all pla-ces;

со-кро-ви-ще бла-гих и жиз-ни по-да-те-лю
O treas'-ry of good things, and giv-er of Life,_____

при-и-ди и все-ли-ся в ны и о-чи-сти ны от
come and cleanse us from ev'-ry stain, and take up thine a-bode

310

вся-ки-я сквер - ны и спа-си Бла-же ду - ши на - - ша.
in us, O God___ and save our souls O Ho - ly___ One!

175

Traditional Bulgarian chant

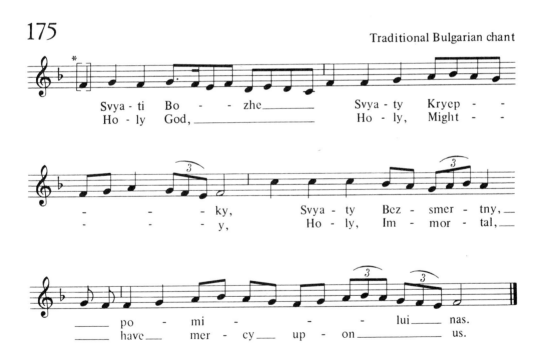

Svya - ti Bo - - zhe___ Svya - ty Kryep - -
Ho - ly God, ___ Ho - ly, Might - -

- - - ky, Svya - ty Bez - smer - tny, __
- - - y, Ho - ly, Im - mor - tal, __

___ po - mi - - - - lui___ nas.
___ have__ mer - cy__ up - on___ us.

*This note is to be used only when German is sung.

311

Russian Orthodox Liturgy

Во цар - - стви - и тво - ем
Re - mem - ber thy ser - vants, Lord,

по - мя - ни нас Гос - по - ди.
when com - est thy glo - rious reign.

Бла - жен - - ни ни - щи - и ду - хом
Bless - ed ____ are the poor in spi - rit;

я - котех есть цар - ство не - бес - но - е.
For ____ the heav - en - ly King - dom is theirs.

2. Блаженни плачущии яко тии утешаться. / Блаженни кротции яко тии наследят землю. / Блаженни алчущшии и жаждущшии правды яко тии насытятся. / Блаженни милостивии яко тии помилованы будут. / Блаженни чистии сердцем яко тии Бога узрят. / Блаженни миротворцы яко тии сынове Божии нарекутся. / Блаженни изгнанны правды ради яко тех есть царство небесное. / Блаженни есте егда поносят вас и изженут и рекут всяк зол глагол на вы лжуще Мене ради. / Радуйтеся и веселитеся яко мзда ваша многа на небеси.

2. Blessed are they that do mourn; / for their Lord shall wipe away their tears. Blessed in Him are the meek; / for their heritage shall be the earth. Blessed are they that seek righteousness; / in that great day their thirst shall be quenched. / Blessed are they that show mercy; / for God shall be merciful unto them. Blessed are the pure in heart; / for in that day shall they see their God. Blessed are they that make peace; / for they shall be called children of God. Blessed those who suffer for Him; / the righteous own the Kingdom of Heav'n. Blessed ye whom men revile; / this world shall persecute you for me. Rejoice, be ye glad in God; / for in Heaven great is your reward.

M. M. Gowen, 1949

177

Traditional Roumanian

A - li - lu - i - a, ___ A - li - lu - i - a, A - li - lu - i - a.

ΘΩΚ ΤΕ ϮϪΟΜ ΝΕΜ ΠΙΩΟΥ ΝΕΜ ΠΙⲤΜΟΥ ΝΕΜ ΠΙΑΜΑϨΙ ϢΑ
ΕΝΕϨ, ΑΜΗΝ: ΕΜΜΑΝΟΥΗΛ ΠΕΝΝΟΥϮ ΠΕΝΟΥΡΟ, ΘΩΚ ΤΕ
ϮϪΟΜ ΝΕΜ ΠΙΩΟΥ ΝΕΜ ΠΙⲤΜΟΥ ΝΕΜ ΠΙΑΜΑϨΙ ϢΑ ΕΝΕϨ,
ΑΜΗΝ: ΠΑϬΟΙⲤ ΙΗⲤΟΥⲤ ΠΙΧΡΙⲤΤΟⲤ ΠΑⲤΩΤΗΡ Ⲛ̄ΑΓΑΘΟⲤ,
ΘΩΚ ΤΕ ϮϪΟΜ ΝΕΜ ΠΙΩΟΥ ΝΕΜ ΠΙⲤΜΟΥ ΝΕΜ ΠΙΑΜΑϨΙ
ϢΑ ΕΝΕϨ ΑΜΗΝ.

179

O - san - na khen Ni - yet - aho - sy: fay pe ep - shi - ry____
Ho - san - na in the high - est: for He is called the____

en Da - vid:____ ef - es ma - ro - ot en - je fith - ni - yo: khen e -
Son of Da - vid; O bless - ed is He, He who com - eth____ in the

fran em - ep - chois en - te____ ni - - gom. Ef - ez · mo e - ron
name__ of Him, the____ Lord__ of ____ Hosts. O may God e - ver

en - jef - no - ty: ten - naz - mo èp e - fran eth - o - owab:____ en -
bless His sons and may we e - ver bless__ His ho - ly name:____

- si - yo ni - ven e - re pef - ez - mo: Na - sho - pi ef - nin e -
His prais - es e - ver - more re - sound: Through all time and through e -

- vol____ khen - ron. Ef - ez ma rot en - je Ef -
- ter - ni - - ty. O may we laud the Fa - ther

[continued overleaf

- yot nem Ep - shi - ry: nem Ep - hev - ma____ eth - o - wab:____
and the____ Son and al - so laud the____ Ho - ly Spi - rit,

ti et - ri -yas as - gik e - vol: ten - o - osht em - mos ten -
three in____One and__ One in__ three: we a - dore and glo - ri -

- ti - o - nas Ky - ri ye - lei - son, Ky - ri
- fy ___ thy ___ name. Ky - ri - e - lei - son, Ky - ri -

ye - lei - son, _____ Ky ri ___ ye - lei - - son.
- e - lei - son, _____ Ky - ri - e - lei - - son.

ⲰⲤⲀⲚⲚⲀ ϦⲈⲚ ⲚⲎⲈⲦϬⲞⲤⲒ: ⲪⲀⲒ ⲠⲈ ⲠϢⲎⲢⲒ Ⲛ̅ⲆⲀⲨⲒⲆ:
ϤⲤ̅ⲘⲀⲢⲰⲞⲨⲦ Ⲛ̅ⲬⲈ ⲪⲎⲈⲐⲚⲎⲞⲨ: ϦⲈⲚ ⲪⲢⲀⲚ Ⲙ̅ⲠϬⲞⲒⲤ Ⲛ̅ⲦⲈ
ⲚⲒϪⲞⲘ ϤⲈⲤⲘⲞⲨ ⲈⲢⲞⲚ Ⲛ̅ⲬⲈ ⲪⲚⲞⲨϮ ⲦⲈⲚⲤⲘⲞⲨ ⲈⲠⲈϤⲢⲀⲚ
ⲈⲐⲞⲨⲀⲂ: Ⲛ̅ⲤⲎⲞⲨ ⲚⲒⲂⲈⲚ ⲈⲢⲈ ⲠⲈϤⲤⲘⲞⲨ: ⲚⲀϢⲰⲠⲒ ⲈϤⲘⲎⲚ
ⲈⲂⲞⲖ ϦⲈⲚ ⲢⲰⲚ. ϤⲤ̅ⲘⲀⲢⲰⲞⲨⲦ Ⲛ̅ⲬⲈ ⲪⲒⲰⲦ ⲚⲈⲘ ⲠϢⲎⲢⲒ: ⲚⲈⲘ
ⲠⲒⲠⲚⲈⲨⲘⲀ ⲈⲐⲞⲨⲀⲂ: ϮⲦⲢⲒⲀⲤ ⲈⲤⲬⲎⲔ ⲈⲂⲞⲖ: ⲦⲈⲚⲞⲨⲰϢⲦ
Ⲙ̅ⲘⲤ ⲦⲈⲚϮⲰⲞⲨ ⲚⲀⲤ ⲔⲨⲢⲒⲈ ⲈⲖⲈⲎⲤⲞⲚ ⲔⲨⲢⲒⲈ ⲈⲖⲈⲎⲤⲞⲚ ⲔⲨⲢⲒⲈ
ⲈⲖⲈⲎⲤⲞⲚ

180

Europe
Ancient Gallican melody

(Preferably unaccompanied)

Ky - ri - e e - le - i - son, Chri - ste e - le - i - son,

Ky - ri - e e - le - i - son.

181

France
J. Berthier

Gloire à Dieu, Paix aux hom-mes, Joie du ciel sur la ter - re.
Praise to God! Peace to all men, joy to earth comes from hea - ven!

1. Pour tes mer-veil - les, Sei - gneur Dieu, ton peu - ple te rend
1. For all your won-ders, O Lord God, your peo - ple come to

grâ - ce. A - mi des hom - mes, sois bé - ni
thank___ you. Our gra - cious friend, we bless your name,

pour ton rè - gne qui vient! A toi les chants de
for your King - dom which comes! To you we bring our

D.C.

fê - te par ton fils bien ai - mé, dans___ l'Es - prit.
prai - ses through the love of the Son and of the Spirit.

2. Sauveur de monde, Jésus-Christ, / écoute nos prières. / Agneau de Dieu,
Vainqueur du mal, / sauve-nous du péché. / Dieu saint, splendeur du Père, /
Dieu vivant, le Très Haut, le Seigneur.

J. Berthier

2. The world's redeemer, Jesus Christ, / receive the prayer we bring you. / O Lamb
of God, you conquered death; / now have mercy on us. / Most Holy Jesus, Son
of God: / living Lord of all worlds, our Lord God!

Erik Routley 1972

319

France
Joseph Gelineau and Michel Chappuis 1957
arr. David Goodall 1970

182

Unison

O - - mnes gen - tes plaud - i - te ma - ni -
All___ you peo - ple cheer___ with voice ___ and

-bus _____ Ju - bi - la - te De - -
hands_____ and re - joice___ in God___ the

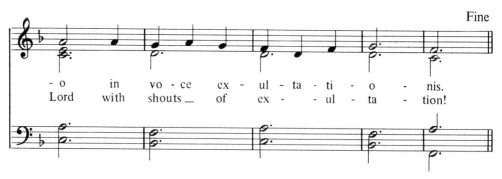

Fine

- o in vo - ce ex - ul - ta - ti - o - nis.
Lord with shouts _ of ex - - ul - ta - tion!

From Psalm 47 and Revelation 5

O - mnes_ gen - tes plau - di - te ma - ni - bus:
Bless - ing and ho - nour and glo - ry and po - wer,

rex ma - gnus su - per o - mnem ter - ram_
all bless - ing and ho - nour and glo - ry and

sub - je - cit_ po - pu - los no - bis pe - di - bus no - stris_
pow'r be un - to him_ that _ sits on the throne and_

D.C. al Fine

_ spe - ciem Ja - cob quam_ di - le - xit!
_ to the Lamb for e - ver and e - ver!

183

France
Association Episcopale Liturgique
Harm. C.D.

A toi le rè - gne! A toi la puis-sance et la

gloi - re pour les siè - cles des siè - cles!

184

France
Joseph Gelineau 1971
Composed for C.D.

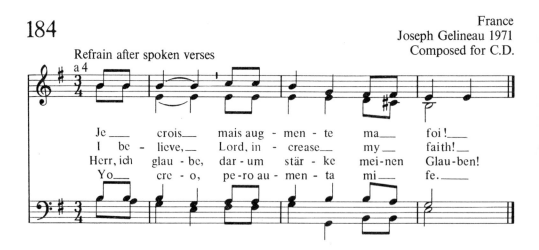

Refrain after spoken verses

Je ___ crois ___	mais aug - men - te	ma ___ foi! ___
I be - lieve, ___	Lord, in - crease ___	my ___ faith! ___
Herr, ich glau - be,	dar - um stär - ke	mei-nen Glau-ben!
Yo ___ cre - o,	pe -ro au - men - ta	mi ___ fe. ___

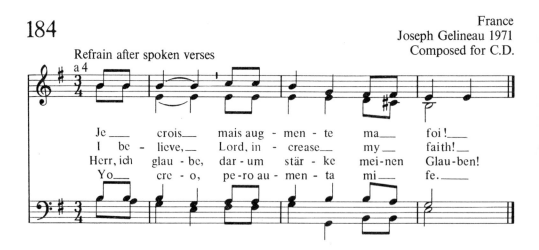

1. Je crois en Dieu le Père tout-puissant, / créateur du ciel et de la terre.

2. Je crois en Jésus-Christ, / son fils unique, notre Seigneur, / qui est né de la Vierge Marie, / a souffert la passion, été enseveli, / est ressuscité d'entre les morts / et qui est assis à la droite du Père.

3. Je crois en l'Esprit Saint, / à la sainte Eglise universelle, / à la communion des saints, / à la remission des péchés, / à la resurrection de la chair, / et à la vie éternelle.

185

Europe
Vatican XVII

(Preferably unaccompanied)

Unison

San-ctus,__ San-ctus,__ San-ctus Do-mi-nus De-us Sa-ba-oth.

Ple-ni sunt cae-li et ter-ra glo-ri-a tu-a.___

Ho-san-na in ex-cel-sis. Be-ne-di-ctus__ qui ve-nit

in no-mi-ne Do-mi-ni. Ho-san-na in ex-cel-sis.__

186 Jubilate

U.S.A.
John Erickson 1971

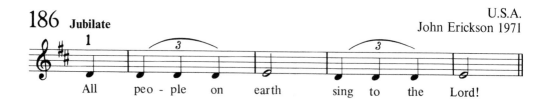

All peo - ple on earth sing to the Lord!

For he is our God.

Joy! joy! joy! joy! joy! joy!

His_____ truth is_____ love.

324

Gloria

Organ

Glo - ry to the Fa - ther ___ and to the Son ___ and to the Ho - ly Spi - rit; as in the be - gin - ning, so now ___ and for e - ver. A - men.

The four phrases of this JUBILATE may be sung as a canon, or they may be performed aleatorically. In the latter case four groups should be formed, perhaps in different parts of the room. At the signal to begin, each group sings one of the phrases over and over again, beginning pianissimo, rising to fortissimo. The organ or other instruments should begin to improvise under the singing when it has been going for a minute or two, and should build up to a decisive chord, fortissimo, which is then abruptly released. This is the signal for the whole congregation to take up the GLORIA which follows.

187

U.S.A.
John Erickson 1969

Unison, rich and full

Ho - ly, Ho - ly, Ho - ly

Lord, God of pow'r___ and might, heav'n and

earth are full___ of your glo - ry. Ho

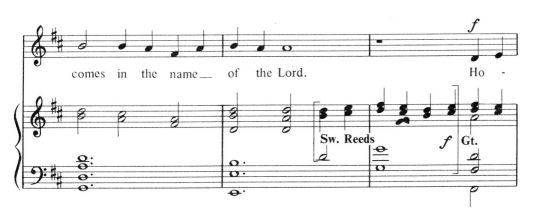

Rounds and Canons · Rundgesänge und Kanons
Canons

188

Germany
Herbert Beuerle 1967

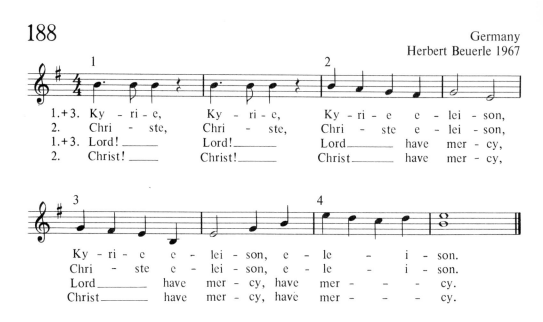

1.+3. Ky - ri - e,   Ky - ri - e,   Ky - ri - e   e - lei - son,
2.   Chri - ste,   Chri - ste,   Chri - ste   e - lei - son,
1.+3. Lord! ____   Lord! ____   Lord ____ have mer - cy,
2.   Christ! ____   Christ! ____   Christ ____ have mer - cy,

Ky - ri - e   e - lei - son,   e - le -   i - son.
Chri - ste   e - lei - son,   e - le -   i - son.
Lord ____ have mer - cy,   have mer -   cy.
Christ ____ have mer - cy,   have mer -   cy.

189

Germany
Adam Gumpelzhaimer 1559–1625

Neig dein Ohr zu mir,   mein Gott, und sei mir gnä - dig, Herr Je - su,
Au - di, Do - mi - ne,   et mi - se - re - re me - i, Do - mi - ne
Bow thine ear to me,   have mer - cy on thy ser - vant, Lord Je - sus

hilf mir in al - len   mei - nen Nö - ten. - ten.
Je - su, tu sis ad - iu - tor me - us. - us.
help me in all my tri - bu - la - tion. - tion.

190

Germany
Albert Thate

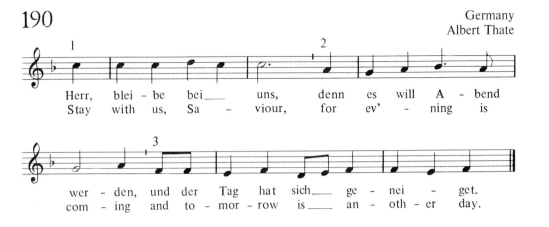

Herr, blei - be bei___ uns, denn es will A - bend
Stay with us, Sa - viour, for ev' - ning is

wer - den, und der Tag hat sich___ ge - nei - get.
com - ing and to - mor - row is___ an - oth - er day.

191

Germany
Richard Rudolf Klein 1964

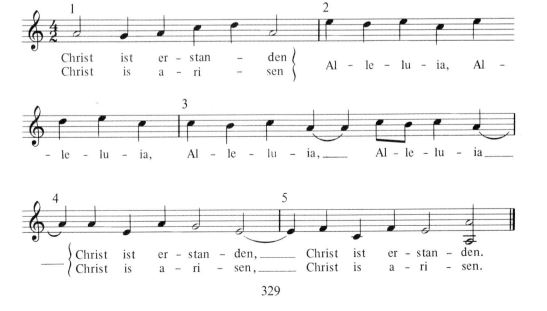

Christ ist er - stan - den Al - le - lu - ia, Al -
Christ is a - ri - sen

- le - lu - ia, Al - le - lu - ia,___ Al - le - lu - ia___

Christ ist er - stan - den,___ Christ ist er - stan - den.
Christ is a - ri - sen,___ Christ is a - ri - sen.

192

Jé - sus Christ est né, il est né au - jourd'- hui!

Jé - sus Christ est né, il est né au - jourd'-hui! - jourd'-hui!

Jé - sus Christ est né, il est né au - jourd' - hui.

193

Indian

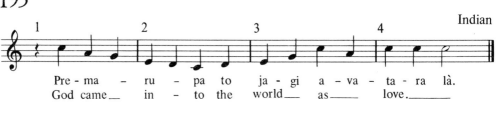

Pre - ma - ru - pa to ja - gi a - va - ta - ra là.
God came in - to the world as love.

Germany
Paul Ernst Ruppel
Melody based on „Macht hoch die Tür"
(Freylinghausen 1715)

194

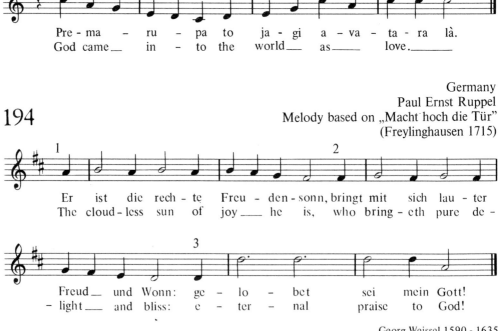

Er ist die rech - te Freu - den - sonn, bringt mit sich lau - ter
The cloud - less sun of joy he is, who bring - eth pure de -

Freud und Wonn: ge - lo - bet sei mein Gott!
- light and bliss: e - ter - nal praise to God!

Georg Weissel 1590 - 1635
(E) Catherine Winkworth 1863

330

195

U.S.A.
Lee Hastings Bristol, Jr. 1970

The Lord is my shep – herd, my guard – ian, my guide. What – so –
– ev – er I want he doth sure – ly pro – vide. Ev – er
since I was born,__ it is he__ that hath crowned the
life that he gave me with bless – ings all round.

Lee Hastings Bristol, Jr.

196

Germany
Hermann Stern 1943

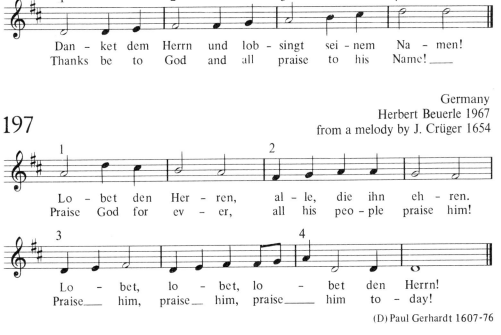

Dan – ket dem Herrn und lob – singt sei – nem Na – men!
Thanks be to God and all praise to his Name!__

Germany
Herbert Beuerle 1967
from a melody by J. Crüger 1654

197

Lo – bet den Her – ren, al – le, die ihn eh – ren.
Praise God for ev – er, all his peo – ple praise him!

Lo – bet, lo – bet, lo – bet den Herrn!
Praise__ him, praise__ him, praise____ him to – day!

(D) Paul Gerhardt 1607-76

198

Germany
Hermann Stern

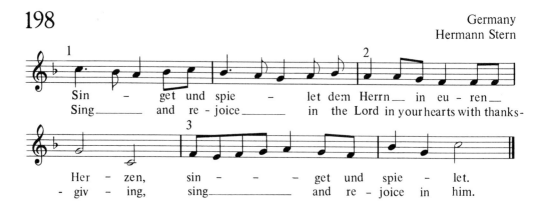

Sin - get und spie - let dem Herrn __ in eu - ren __
Sing _____ and re - joice _____ in the Lord in your hearts with thanks-

Her - zen, sin - - - get und spie - let.
- giv - ing, sing _____ and re - joice in him.

199

Germany
Gerd Watkinson 1955

Herr, un - ser Herr - scher, wie herr - lich ist
O Lord, our Mas - ter, how ex - cel - lent

dein __ Na - me in al - len Lan - den.
is your name _____ in all the world. __

Two Parting Blessings · Schlußsegen
Deux Bénédictions

200

India
Gazar

An Indian Blessing

Ye - shu su - pri - ya,
Je - sus, lov - ing Lord;

Ye - shu a - shra - ye,
Je - sus, strength and stay,

Ye - shu pri - ya ta - ra - ka, sa -
in your mer - cy bless us all and

- ha - ya ho - ma - la.
keep us night and day.

येशू सुप्रिय येशू आश्रया   येशू प्रिय तारका सहाय हो मला

201

An Israeli Blessing

To be sung antiphonally

Israel

A Ge - he ein in dei - nen Frie - den! B Schla - fe dei - nen gu - ten
A Go in peace, and God be with you: B Sleep in peace, God hold you

Schlaf! A Ruh dich aus nach dei - ner Ar - beit, B und ge - seg - net sei die
fast! A Take your ease from dai - ly du - ty; B af - ter la - bour, rest at

Nacht! A Mond - licht fließt her - ab vom Him - mels - zelt, B und der Tau glänzt
last! A Moon - light shares a glimpse of hea - ven's mirth, B dew - fall fresh - ens

auf un - serm Feld. A Preist den Tag und die Nacht! B Preist die
flow - ers of earth. A Thank God for day and night. B Thank God

Nacht und den Tag! Preist die Son - ne, prei - set die Er - de,
for dark and light. For the Sun and for all things liv - ing

preist den Herrn al - ler Wel - ten. A - men! A - men!
to their Lord prais - es giv - ing! A - men! A - men!

(D) Helmut König 1972
(E) Erik Routley 1972

202

Germany
P. E. Ruppel

A - men, A - men, A - men.

Index of Authors and Composers
Verzeichnis der Autoren und Komponisten
Index d'auteurs et compositeurs

Key to symbols and abbreviations · Abkürzungen und Zeichen   Explication des signes et abréviations

Against number	no symbol =	Original text, or text and melody
nach Nummer	kein Zeichen =	Originaltext, oder Text und Melodie
après le numéro	sans signe =	texte originale, ou texte et mélodie
	* =	Translation or paraphrase (text)
		Übersetzung oder Paraphrase (Text)
		Traduction ou paraphrase (texte)
	† =	Arrangement or harmonisation (melody)
		Arrangement oder Harmonisierung (Melodie)
		Arrangement ou harmonsation (melodie)
	italics =	Melody
	Kursiv =	Melodie
	italique =	mélodie
Against names	+ =	Ordained minister or priest
nach Namen		Prêtre, pasteur
après le nom		Priester, Pfarrer

CHURCHES/KIRCHEN/ÉGLISES

Bap	=	Baptist	Ref	=	Reformed
CE	=	Church of England	UCC	=	United Church of Canada
Cong	=	Congregationalist	UCJ	=	United Church of Japan
Disc	=	Disciples of Christ	UN	=	Unitarian
L	=	Lutheran	UF	=	United Free Church (Scotland)
Meth	=	Methodist	URC	=	United Reformed Church
Mor	=	Moravian			(Britain: founded 1972;
Orth	=	Orthodox			formerly Presbyterian and
Prot	=	Protestant			Congregationalist)
RC	=	Roman Catholic			

OTHER ABBREVIATIONS

Bp	=	Bishop	Bischof	Evêque	
Btd	=	Civil servant	Beamter	Fonctionnaire	
CD	=	Cantate Domino, editor			
C.S.Sp	=	Community of the Holy Spirit	Gemeinschaft des Heiligen Geistes	Communauté du Saint Esprit	
Dram	=	Playwright	Dramatiker	Dramaturge	
Ecum	=	Ecumenist			
Ed	=	Educationist	Erzieher	Éducateur	
Hy	=	Hymn writer or editor	Kirchenlieddichter oder Herausgeber	Hymnologiste où rédacteur	
Jour	=	Journalist	Journalist	Journaliste	

Kant	=	Cantor	Kantor	Chanteur
Kmus	=	Church music organizer	Kirchenmusik-direktor	Organisateur de la musique de l'église
Komp	=	Composer	Komponist	Compositeur
Leg	=	Lawyer	Rechtsanwalt	Avocat
Lit	=	Author	Autor	Écrivain
Litg	=	Liturgist	Liturgiker	Liturgiste
M	=	Monastery	Kloster	Monastère
M de fam	=	Housewife	Hausfrau	Mère de famille
Med	=	Doctor	Artzt	Médecin
Mil	=	Army chaplain	Militärpfarrer	Pasteur militaire
Miss	=	Missionary	Missionar	Missionnaire
Mus	=	Musician	Musiker	Musicien
Muscg	=	Musicologist	Musikologue	Musicologist
O.F.M.	=	Franciscan	Franziskaner	Ordre de St François
Org	=	Organist	Organist	Organiste
Philos	=	Philosopher	Philosoph	Philosophe
Pol	=	Politician	Staatsmann	Politicien
Prof	=	Professor	Professor	Professeur
Rev	=	Reviser	Bearbeiter	Réviseur
S.J.	=	Jesuit	Jesuit	Societé de Jésus
Sch	=	Schoolteacher	Lehrer	Instituteur
Scl	=	Scholar	Gelehrte	Savant
Sing	=	Singer	Sänger	Chanteur
Theol	=	Theologian	Theologe	Théologien
Tr	=	Translator	Übersetzer	Traducteur
WCC	=	World Council of Churches: staff or associate	ÖRK-Personal oder Berater	Conseil œcuménique des Églises: Personnel où associé

COUNTRY OF ORIGIN

Ang	=	Anguilla	Ir	=	Ireland
Arg	=	Argentina	It	=	Italy
Bar	=	Barbados	Jam	=	Jamaica
Belg	=	Belgium	Jap	=	Japan
Braz	=	Brazil	Mal	=	Malawi
Camn	=	Cameroon	Nig	=	Nigeria
Can	=	Canada	NL	=	Netherlands
Cz	=	Czechoslovakia	Nor	=	Norway
Ch	=	China	Pers	=	Persia
Den	=	Denmark	Phil	=	Philippines
D	=	Germany/Deutschland	Slo	=	Slovakia
			S	=	Sweden
F	=	France	SL	=	Sri Lanka
Fin	=	Finland	Swi	=	Switzerland
GB	=	Great Britain	Tai	=	Taiwan
Gr	=	Greece	Tanz	=	Tanzania
Hun	=	Hungary	Urug	=	Uruguay
I	=	India	US	=	United States of America
In	=	Indonesia			

Subject Index · Verwendungshinweise
Table analytique

God · Gott · Dieu

His Providence and Promises · Seine Vorsehung und seine Verheißungen · Sa providence et ses promesses No./Nr. 2, 9, 10, 11, 24, 27, 43–52, 115

His Creation · Seine Schöpfung · Sa création No./Nr. 3, 8, 12, 15, 19, 27, 31, 32, 43, 44, 71, 111, 113

His Word · Sein Wort · Sa parole (see also: The Scriptures · siehe auch: Die Heilige Schrift · voir aussi: l'Ecriture) No./Nr. 7, 22, 45, 46

His Reign · Sein Reich · Son règne No./Nr. 6, 17, 21, 113, 146

The Holy Trinity · Die Heilige Dreifaltigkeit · La sainte trinité No./Nr. 119–22, 152, 175, 177, 179, 184, 185, 187, 188

Jesus Christ · Jesus Christus · Jésus Christ

His Advent and Incarnation · Seine Ankunft und seine Menschwerdung · Sa venue et son incarnation No./Nr. 21, 50, 52–65, 152, 165–7, 179, 181, 192, 193

His Ministry and Teaching · Sein Amt und seine Lehre · Son ministère et son enseignement No./Nr. 33, 37, 66–77, 81, 104, 125, 130, 150, 156

His Passion · Sein Leidensweg · Sa passion No./Nr. 14, 40, 78–83, 131, 162

His Resurrection · Seine Auferstehung · Sa résurrection No./Nr. 84–99, 172, 191

His Reign and Glory · Sein Reich und seine Herrlichkeit · Son règne et sa gloire No./Nr. 79, 81, 93–9, 178

The Holy Spirit · Der Heilige Geist · Le Saint-Esprit

The Gifts of the Spirit · Die Gaben des Heilgen Geistes · Les dons de l'Esprit No./Nr. 100–5, 144, 174

The Scriptures · Die Heilige Schrift · L'Ecriture No./Nr. 7, 22, 45, 46, 104, 106, 107

The Church · Die Kirche · L'Eglise

Worship and Praise · Gottesdienst und Lobpreisung · Louange et adoration No./Nr. 1, 3, 6, 13, 16, 18, 21, 25, 28, 47, 57, 108–22, 169, 171, 175, 177, 182, 183, 186, 187, 190, 194, 197, 198

Unity and Mission · Einheit und Sendung · Unité et mission No./Nr. 1, 13, 63, 76, 77, 97–9, 133–50, 164

Penitence · Busse · Pénitence No./Nr. 60, 136, 139, 148

The Sacraments · Die Sakramente · Les sacrements No./Nr. 95

The Eucharist · Das Heilige Abendmahl · L'eucharistie No./Nr. 20, 46, 74, 83, 92, 96, 151–62, 164, 166–87, 195

Morning · Morgen · Matin No./Nr. 120, 128, 129, 132

Evening · Abend · Soir No./Nr. 200, 201

The Saints · Die Heiligen · Les saints No./Nr. 143, 163, 165

Man · Der Mensch · L'homme

The City · Die Stadt · La cité No./Nr. 29, 35, 38, 39, 40, 41

The Earth · Die Welt · Le monde No./Nr. 8, 19, 32, 43

Peace · Frieden · Paix No./Nr. 18, 42, 55, 134, 148

Service and Friendship · Dienst und Freundschaft · Service et fraternité No./Nr. 30, 32, 34, 36–8, 43, 45, 49, 50, 59, 61, 66, 70, 75, 133–5, 138, 145, 151, 160

Justice · Gerechtigkeit · Justice No./Nr. 12, 13, 30, 32, 34, 39, 51, 116

Work · Arbeit · Travail No./Nr. 71, 72, 118, 120, 129, 132, 133

Art · Kunst · Art No./Nr. 116

Index of First Lines
Verzeichnis der Liedanfänge
Répertoire selon les premiers mots

* = Rounds and Canons · Kanons · Canons / † = Liturgical music · Liturgische Musik · Music liturgique
/ § = Antiphonal music · Lieder mit Antiphonen · Musique antiphonée

347

DATE DUE

HIGHSMITH 45-220